FROM FELL & FIELD

Any account of any aspect of agriculture is primarily a human story
George Robinson 'calling in' the cows, Moss End c.1950

FROM FELL & FIELD

A History of
THE WESTMORLAND
COUNTY SHOW
1799 - 1999

by
Roger K. Bingham

CICERONE PRESS LTD
MILNTHORPE, CUMBRIA

© Roger Bingham
ISBN 1 85284 290 3
First published 1999

A catalogue record for this book is available from the British Library

This book is dedicated to
Brigadier C.E. Tyron-Wilson of Dallam Tower
to mark both his 90th birthday and the 200th anniversary of
The County Show founded by his ancestor
Daniel Wilson in 1799

Other books by the same author:
Our village - a pictorial record of Milnthorpe from 1860. (1977)
The Church at Heversham - a history of Westmorland's oldest recorded church.
(1984)
The Chronicles of Milnthorpe. (Cicerone 1987)
Lost Resort? The flow and ebb of Morecambe. (Cicerone 1990)
Kendal: A Social History. (Cicerone 1995)

Cup and medal photographs: Warwick Dickinson Photography

Front cover: Champion shorthorn c.1815. The sketch still in the possession of the
Garnett family is entitled, 'Mr. Christ. Garnett of Low Sizergh'

CONTENTS

❋   ❋   ❋

ACKNOWLEDGEMENTS

History is the record of human affairs which cannot be compiled by just one person; it is never merely 'his' story. All accounts of people's activities are, therefore, necessarily collective tasks though the historian may be entrusted to marshal and write down or word process- the information. No history can ever be complete nor can it be perfect because we cannot know everything and everybody will have different ideas about what is important or should be left out.

Specifically history is the story of the recorded past and is largely dependent on documentary evidence. If this is lacking people's memories become crucial but the chances of errors, omissions and misinterpretation are correspondingly greater. For this history of the Westmorland County Show personal contributions and encouragement have been extraordinarily valuable and I wish to record my gratitude to the people who have readily helped me research and compile - in less than a year - this book which attempts to record not just the story of the Agricultural Society and its Show but something also of the social history of my native county of Westmorland.

In particular I wish to thank for supplying me with information, photographs and ideas: Mrs Moyre Atkinson, Mr Tony Atkinson, Mr Brian Barnes, Mr Robert Bindloss, Mr and Mrs Jim Bland, Mr Brian Ellis, Mrs Margaret Capstick, Mrs Marina Chapman, Mrs Olive Clarke, Cumbria County Library services and especially Mrs Jackie Fay librarian of the Local History collection, Mr and Mrs Tony Duckett, Mr Percy Duff and the trustees of the Margaret Duff Photographic Collection, Warwick Dickinson Photographic Services, Mrs Doreeen Galbraith, Mr and Mrs Wilson Garnett, Mr John Garnett, Mr John Geldard, Mr Tony Gibson, Mr John Handley, Mr and Mrs Chris Harrison-Beck, Mrs Mary Jackson, Kentdale Studios, Mr John Ladell, Mrs Dorothy Lambert, Mr Kevin Lancaster, Mr Fred Martin, Mr and Mrs Wilson Melling, Mr John Park, The Plough Inn, Lupton, Mr George Procter, Mr Rodger Read, Mr George Robinson, Mr Harold Robinson, Dr John Satchell, Mrs Jean Sowerby, Mrs Barbara Stothert, Sir Sanderson Temple, Mr Alan S. Thompson, Brigadier C.E. Tryon-Wilson, The Editor and and Proprietors of the *Westmorland Gazette*, Mr and Mrs Henry Willison and many more whose names may have slipped my memory but to whom I am equally grateful. I also wish to thank especially Mr Tony Atkinson, Mrs Olive Clarke, Mr John Geldard, Mr Tony Duckett, Mr Brian Ellis, Mr Fred Martin, Mr George Procter and Mr Harold Robinson who read much of the text (especially Chapter 5 which deals with their own era) and who made many valuable suggestions.

It is surprising that the show has never before been subject to a full scale historical study. Consequently I must record my indebtedness to the previous brief account written by Mr Stephen Barratt in 1979. Unfortunately now, as in Mr Barratt's time, the records of the Society have been particularly sparse with no archives dating from before c.1894 and I have had to rely largely on the accounts printed in the *Westmorland Gazette*. Inevitably these reports compiled hurriedly for publication the next day have been prone to errors and confusion especially about names and places. Thus a prize winner in different years might be recorded as, for instance Mr G Robinson, Mr G.E. Robinson or Mr George Robinson. Unless I know from other sources that these names refer to the same person they have been indexed separately. Similarly different people with the same recorded name might be indexed and mentioned as the same person. A particular vexation has been place names which the reporter recorded in the way he was told. Thus Helsington was in one case written down as 'Elsington' while Mr Parson of Overthwaite was recorded as coming variously from Beetham (his parish) or Holme (his nearest village) or Milnthorpe (his postal address). In these cases I have been able to work out to where or to whom the report referred but in others I could not be certain and so I kept to the names as originally recorded. For these and other inconsistencies, mistakes and omissions I apologise but my overwhelming sentiment remains that of gratitude to my fellow Westmerians who have made my task in writing *From Fell and Field: a history of the Westmorland County Show 1799-1999* a labour of love.

Above right: *Westmorland Coat of Arms*

CHAPTER ONE

Westmorland before 1799

Westmorland's geography and, therefore, its agriculture is summed up in its name. Everywhere the old county's landscape is dominated by moorland, which sprawls up and around the rugged terrain that links the western slopes of the Pennine chain with the Lake District massif. To the north the mountains and moors fall towards the Eden Valley and the Solway coastal plain while in the south they descend through Kentdale and Lunesdale and other river valleys to the bumpy drumlins and mosses around Morecambe Bay. Buffeted by winds from the Irish Sea and the Atlantic much of the land is bleak and, invariably, in this the region of England's highest rainfall, all of it is wet. Though hailed for its wild beauty even the most mountainous terrain is not wild in an agricultural sense for all unbuilt on land is farmed. As is shown by the laser straight walls, roller coasting up and down the slopes, people have shaped the landscape so that it can be cultivated. Before the most isolated flocks could graze in safety on the most far-flung heaf human beings had to go there first. Just as farming folk fashioned the land so that it could graze their stock and grow their crops so too the rewards and punishments of tilling an often stingy soil have moulded their character and outlook. Hence any account of any aspect of agriculture is primarily a human story.

Fittingly the old county was called not after its appearance but after the people who lived there. They were the 'Westmoringas' - the folk beyond the western mountains who in the seventh century had come under the rule of the Angles of the Kingdom of Northumbria away to the east. Then as before and after them the inhabitants of Westmorland were but partly, or in name only, influenced by others. Nominally their county and those villages with such place name endings as ham, by and ton spoke of an Anglian latter day English heritage but in fact the Celtic Cwmry, descendants of the pre-historic Brigantes, continued to hold sway in their ancient homeland. Already they had remained largely untouched by earlier Roman rule and, in scattered settlements, they had

7

A far flung heaf on the land of the western moors

evolved their own way of life. Though they remained largely detached from their conquerors they fed and clothed them. It was barley and oats grown in Kentdale and not wheat from Italy and Gaul that filled the granaries of the Roman fort at Watercrook near Kendal. Some 2000 mutton and beef bones also found at Watercrook along with fragments of 'Roman' leather and even of wool excavated elsewhere in the region show that sheep and cattle were already the mainstays of local farming.

Three centuries after the Angles had penetrated the post Roman Celtic tribe lands the Vikings, around 900 AD, infused the region with its most distinctive cultural ingredient. Having first come as furiously bloodthirsty raiders these Norsemen later stayed on as settlers occupying and cultivating spare land close to but yet apart from the host community. Inevitably within a generation or two nature took its course; the communities merged so that in the veins of native Westmerians there circulates the blood of Celt, Angle and Viking. Yet, a thousand years after the mingling of the races, the vocabulary of the Norsemen survived to enrich the spoken heritage of Westmorland with a Scandinavian twang that proclaims that Westmorland is no mere Anglo-Saxon part of England. Villages which grew from their woodland clearings are still called thwaites; their hillsides are still known as slacks and bracks; stock is still led from indoor shippons or from outside folds, parrocks, crofts and cotes to pastures further away called erghs, wicks or stints. Westmorland's streams are becks, gills or sykes; its marshes are mosses; its lakes tarns or meres; its cliffs are scars and the town streets are gates. Above all, in every sense, the Vikings gave the name of fells to the mountains and moors that in every Westmorland parish link the

A scene for the pastoral poets.
Longhorns watering at Elterwater c.1820

sparse lowlands with the cloudy skies. Well into the era of the 'pastoral' poets, when Westmorland was discovered by the wider world of tourism and English Literature, shepherds counted their sheep in the Nordic numerals: 'Yoan, Tyan, Taed'ere, Mimp'. Two centuries later the persistent use of 'thees and thous' along with the diminutives of th' and t' in the everyday speech especially of farming folk tell of an adherence to older usage abandoned long since elsewhere.

Always on the edge of England Westmorland has often been late in moving with the times especially if so called 'progress' is set by 'them fra' away' or by 'off-comers'. But if sometimes Westmerians have been slow in the uptake they exhibit the reverse characteristics of staying power and of holding fast to the traditions of their forebears. Such tenacity is shown by their attachment to the name of their county even after it had been swept off the map of England. Westmorland people remain proud of their birth right, perhaps, partly because there are fewer Westmerians than natives of any other English county - for although Westmorland was not the smallest in size it always had the lowest population. A quarter of a century after Westmorland (in 1974), for 'administrative reasons', was absorbed along with parts of Lancashire, Yorkshire and all of Cumberland into the new County of Cumbria a host of titles survive to remind residents and visitors alike that they are still in the old county. Hence we have a Westmorland General Hospital, a Westmorland Shopping Centre, 'The Westmorland Gazette' and a Parliamentary Constituency of Westmorland and Lonsdale.

Few of these other 'Westmorland' institutions unite the county, the land and its people better or more closely with the past and present than does the Westmorland County Show. This 'County' Show was born out of the earlier Kendal Show founded in 1799 and is one of the oldest Agricultural Shows in the Kingdom.

It is to mark the 1999 Bi-centenary of 'The Show' that this history has been written. By so doing it is hoped to keep alive the honoured memory and living traditions of Westmorland while recording the often hard won achievements of Westmerians on the lands of the western moors.

The birth of the show in 1799 coincided with the start of the era when for the first time the beauties of the Westmorland wilderness were beginning to be extolled by poets and painters. Eighty years earlier when Daniel Defoe described a journey through the county he did not once mention the Lakes. Instead, obviously horrified, he wrote of a 'country eminent only for being the wildest and most barren and frightful of any that I have passed through bounded by a chain of almost impassable mountains which in the language of the people are called fells'. An oasis existed around Kendal for, Defoe found, Kentdale was 'a pleasant and fruitful land'. Other commentators also contrasted the barbarous and barren moors with the cultivated tranquillity of the lowlands. Thus in 1794 Andrew Pringle in his 'General View of the Agriculture of the County of Westmorland', having dismissed much of the County as being so 'mountainous that a great proportion of it must ever remain untouched', conceded that there were, nevertheless, several 'very pleasant vallies (sic) that want only trees and hedge rows to be truly beautiful'. Another major commentator on Westmorland agriculture around 1799 was Richard Watson Bishop of Llandaff. The Bishop despite his Episcopal title was a native of Westmorland and notoriously he spent more time on the 'pastoral' duty of improving his Calgarth estate, on Windermere than he did with his 'flock' in his distant Welsh diocese.

He was both censorious and optimistic about the local scene. Of the fells he moaned 'it is difficult to behold the desolate state in which they lie without surprise at the nation having so long delayed taking measures for their improvement'. Specifically he observed that 'to the north of Shap lies a very extensive common called scars where between two or three thousand acres of level white land in a state of nature offend the eye...and cry aloud for improvement. Near the mouth of the river Kent there is a marsh of considerable extent at Heversham and Milthrope (sic) overstocked but if the sea was banked off it would produce corn lands or if a reasonable stint would enable better stock to be produced'. Regarding the uplands he advocated plantations of larches. Westmorland's relatively treeless state had long been notorious. Nicolson and Burn in 1774 had suggested that the reason for there being 'no great plenty of wood' was because the trees 'had been industriously destroyed to prevent (them) affording shelter to the Scotch invaders'. Even older records concern the arable barrenness of the County. Speed in 1611 wrote that Westmorland was 'not to be commended either for plenty of corn or cattle being neither stored with arable ground to bring forth the one, nor pasturage to bring forth the other'. Pringle added a quasi-scientific weight to the view that Westmorland was virtually a Wilderness. Taking the county's dimensions as being 32 miles from Penrith in the north to Burton in the south and 40 miles from east to west, he calculated that it consisted of 33,139,840 statute acres or a 73rd part of England but only 100,000 acres was sufficiently productive to earn a rental of around £1 per acre. Thus 'between half and three-quarters of the land (was) virtually uncultivated though even the roughest high enclosed pastures were let at 5s per acre'. In North Westmorland 'field sheep' were rare and at Great Asby it was said that there were 10,500 sheep on the fells compared to 500 in the village pastures. Virtually all the nurture afforded by the mean ground was consumed before winter set in. So sparse was grass even on the comparably lush fells towards Furness that William West noted that holly groves were planted purposely to provide sheep with winter forage. According to William Pearson the 'stints' on most commons were 'so keenly shaved...that from morn to eve it's nibble, nibble, nibble. If a poorman's horse had lost half an hour it would have been fatal!'

Squabbles over stints were interminable:

'We've fratched and scaulded lang and sair, about our reights on't fell,
The number of our sheep, and whaur the heaf was they sud dwell...
And oft we fratched and fret about, and throppled uddar sair,
Upon the whol' the fell hes meade mischief for iver mair'.

Anciently the fells' agricultural sterility had been alleviated by culling readily available wild life. Red Deer bones found at Watercrook show that venison was occasionally on the Roman menu. In Medieval times Gilbert Fitz-Reinfred and Helwise his wife paid 6 stags as rent for land at Spittle which incidentally was close to the site occupied for a hundred years by the Kendal Show. To the north of the town there were 'pleasant woods and gardens at Burneside...with grounds full of fallow deer - and - brave pasties made from...reed (red)...deer on the mountains' where also there abounded 'white wild cattle with black ears (found) only on the moors'. Wild boar were equally plentiful in South Westmorland and their tusks and other porcine remains dating from c. 500AD have been found in the Dog Hole on Haverbrack near Beetham while the name of neighbouring Heversham could derive from 'eofor' the Old English name for boar. By the turn

A Westmorland 'wild cow' c.1799

of the eighteenth century wild boar were barely a memory as traditionally the last one had been hunted to death at Crook in the early 1600's. As for the deer: park walls and savage Game Laws ensured that they were the preserves of the genteel and rapacious hunting classes.

To the difficulties of winning a living from the starveling earth were added the everlasting problems created for the farmer by the wet climate. Westmorland 'lying near the western ocean is much exposed to Rain brought by the South West winds which blow in this part two thirds of the year.' Hence, Nicolson and Burn concluded 'their crops are later by three, four or in some places six weeks than in some other parts of the kingdom'. Good crops were 'hard come by' even in the more favoured areas. Adam Walker observed that the Lune valley near Kirkby Lonsdale 'consists principally of grass farms which is certainly wise conformity to the climate and the country: for crops of corn must be very uncertain where so much rain falls and where the winter sets in so early'. William Hutchinson similarly extolled Westmorland's Eden where 'the valley meadows and pasture grounds are beautiful; but there is little tillage, it having been a received opinion for ages past that grain would not ripen or come to perfection so near the moors...as...a continuous vapour is bourne into the valley, which blights the corn in its blossom.'

Ironically Westmorland's sodden climate put the county in one respect ahead of its times for a continuous tabulation of rainfall has been kept since the great scientist John Dalton recorded Kendal's monthly rainfall throughout 1788. In that year Kendal had a mere 39 inches of rain but in 1789 there were 69 inches. Over the next 60 years the annual average was 53 inches and for the second 60 years i.e. until 1908 it was 49 inches. Rainfall elsewhere, over similar lengthy periods, averaged 81 inches in Grasmere, 63 in Windermere but, as it was in the lee of Lakeland Fells, Kirkby Stephen and the Eden Valley had a 'mere' 40 inches.

'Black drizzling days that blot out the face of things' as Wordsworth put it meant that at times the sun hardly seemed to shine. The 'old grey' town of Kendal averages 1200 hours of sunshine a year, ahead of the 900 hours of parts of inner Lakeland but fatally far behind the 2000 hours per year of the corn lands of East Anglia and the South East. Alleviating the meteorological gloom of Kentdale the rain clouds helped insulate its meadows from the worst of the winter frosts. In some years in Kentdale the temperature only dipped below freezing point on 40 days but periodically a climatic swing could transform normally temperate dales into a sub Arctic region for months on end. There were 13 weeks of frost in 1739-40 and snow drifts cut Kendal off from its surrounding villages for a fortnight. Half of the county's flocks were lost in winter snows of 1798 while blossom did not appear on the damson trees in the neighbouring Lyth Valley until 8th of May, six to eight weeks later than normal. Up on the fells snow was known to fall in eight months even in a good year and when it melted it took weeks on end for the ground to thaw out. Damp and rain could drain but slowly through the lower layers of semi perma frost so the farmsteads were engulfed for much of the spring in a miry mess of mud and dung described pithily as 'clarty'.

Commentators invariably haling from warmer and drier climes often patronisingly pronounced that the climate was good for the people who lived there. Richard Watson, though himself a Westmerian, while admitting that the climate is 'somewhat (!) sharp and severe' it was 'withal very healthful and people live commonly to a very great age.. and though barren as the soil is in many places the county is very populous in proportion to the value of the lands than any other county in the Kingdom'. Later demographers would disagree with this view. According to the first census of 1801 there were about 41,000 inhabitants in the county. Of these about a third lived in the larger market towns of Kendal, Appleby, Kirkby Stephen and Ambleside. Smaller towns and villages accounted for another third. Milnthorpe, at that time Westmorland's only port, had a population of over 1500, a figure which was not exceeded until the 1960's. Even in widespread parishes people could cluster together. In Ravenstonedale, one of the county's most extensive and, therefore, statistically most sparsely

Scattered farmsteads in Longsleddale

inhabited parishes, more than half its population of about 800 lived within a mile of each other in the valley bottom. Nevertheless, most Westmerians lived either in tiny hamlets or in far flung farmsteads economically and socially isolated. Westmorland was famed for having a Grammar School under every hill side and standards of education were relatively high with a male literacy rate at 40% in c.1800. But the further up a valley a farmer's lad lived increased proportionately the chances that he would remain as unlettered as the labouring poor - or women. Moreover the educational value of the Church was also nullified by huge parishes where some farms could be five or even ten miles from a congregation. Service registers prove that 'every body going to Church three times on Sundays' is a myth. In Patterdale farmers from a group of families had a rota so that one man went to church every Sunday. After worship the 'delegate' then trailed what news he'd gathered round the Dale. Being cut off from other folk also made working life difficult. Sometimes there was not enough for the farmer's family to do but as they lived too far away from the labour market they could not get work on a day to day basis easily. Domestic industry might fill any gaps in the grind of agricultural toil. Inventories of the belongings of most Lakeland farmers include looms, spinning wheels and the general tackle of textile manufacture. Amongst 'trade utensils' of Thomas Gardner of Lambrigge who died in 1690 were 'Plow gear 10/- husbandry gear £1. 6. 0. Spinning Wheel and Cards 6/-...ropes and traces 4/-, Wool and line (linen), Line Wheel and Cloth Bag 3/-. Thomas Preston of Milthrope Husbandman goods included a Harrow Barrow 2/6,...Wheel Benches, Shelves, Guilded Balls 15/-'. What the latter were for is not recorded but John Somervell in 'Some Westmorland Wills' suggested they might have belonged to the testator's son! More likely he was one of Westmorland's clockmakers some of whom, like Jonas Barber of Winster, earned national fame though their craft was conducted part time in a barn alongside the other farm buildings. Other handicraft implements like 'wimbles and Turning tools, throe and wheels (lathes), Wheel Nayles and Carving tools' also occur. In Lakeland many a man whittled away a winter's evening by wood carving. Stencils could be bought at local fairs for a whole host of lozenged and swirled panels and initial boards mostly dated from between 1660 and 1720 which often served to decorate built in spice cupboards or dower chests and court cupboards that became the prized heirlooms of many a farming family.

Wood carving apart other non-agricultural work is also shown by references to tanning equipment. In 1670 the magistrates confiscated 23 hides of tanned leather from Quaker John Pearson of Powbank when he refused to pay a fine of £20. Even heavier subsidiary work is indicated in the will of George Dixon of The Heaning Windermere as, in his 1704 will, he left, at his Little Langdale farm (which was near an iron ore deposit), 'a pair of Large Bellows at ye Smelthouse and some wood at ye forge 14/-'.

To the east of the county lighter but incessant work was that undertaken by the knitters of hose and stockings of which 3000 pairs were brought each week from Eden and Dentdale to Kendal market, the man at the reins and the women folk on the cart all knitting as they drove into town! Thus even when the climate prevented the land from bringing forth its increase rural hands were rarely idle and so the fell folk toiled for much of the night as well as throughout all of every day.

Men and women grafted equally hard together. Pringle for instance regretted

that girls made up for the lack of (other) draft animals: 'it is painful to see the serving maids of this country toiling in the severe labour of the field. They drive the harrows and nay it is not uncommon to see sweating at the dung cart, a girl, whose elegant features,

Pool Bank, 'Powbank',
Witherslack

15

A field sledge, Grisedale c.1820

and delicate nicely proportioned limbs seemingly but ill accord with such rough employment'.

Man (and woman) power was essential because wheeled transport was more or less useless as there were few real roads and, where they existed, they were often impassable. At Troutbeck in 1730 the Magistrates were told that the road was 'soe much out of repair that a great part of it is not passable for man or horse to travel...without the danger of being bogged in the moss or lamed among the stones'. In 1745 the loyalist forces were so impeded through 'dirt and decay and want of reparation' of the King's highway over Shap that they failed in their pursuit of the Bonnie Prince Charlie 'by reason that a great number of carriages and four wheeled wagons...could not be forwarded because of the badness of the road' - and this was the main road barely ten miles from the county's main town of Kendal! Until the late eighteenth century pack horses - which were really ponies - were used for carrying most goods. In 1776 Nicolson and Burn recorded that the 'trains' of pack horses setting off daily from Kendal bound for London could number up to 350 animals. On more local journeys such as from Kendal to Hawkshead pack horse trains were smaller but if it had not been for the 'hacks' or panniers on the backs of the sturdy animals any trade would have been impossible. On the fells and around the farms sledges augmented back power even beyond the snowy seasons. They were still in use after 1800 when the first genteel tourists - the 'Lakers' - were amused by the spectacle of women sledgers leading bracken down the fellsides.

Added to women's so called 'manual' labour was, of course, the labour of childbirth. 'The upland fringes of the mountains' were said to 'breed hardy Dalesmen and Daleswomen - fertile in the production of large families'. Despite legends that a Westmorland farming lad would not marry until he had proved that his girl was fertile and, therefore, capable of producing the work force for the next generation, 'forced marriages' were no more common in the county than elsewhere. Indeed the marriage registers show that the age of most grooms was about thirty and possibly indicates that small holdings induced continence as men could not afford to bring up a family until their own siblings were reared and at least one parent was dead. Illegitimate birth rates at a county average of 10% were quite high but were mainly amongst the - geographically - more mobile servant girls and hired labourers called, ironically, 'husbandmen'. Often working in one place for only six months at a time a hired man could move miles away from "t lass he'd gitten wrang'. When this happened illiteracy and bad communications impeded any attempts by the expectant mother or the Guardians of The Poor to track him down and force him 'to do the right thing by't poor lass'.

Child bearing for all married couples of 'breeding' age was an annual occurrence but so too in most years was infant mortality. When John Somervell analysed the make up of over 60 Quaker families living and dying between c.1680 and 1740 he was 'struck by the number of surviving children mentioned, averaging approximately two, pointing - in an age of large families - to a high death rate, even in healthy country surroundings'. Church registers tell a similar sorry story. Occasionally disease massacred a whole generation of innocents as in the Autumn of 1746 when 27 children died at Milnthorpe. Even in 'good years', however, according to the same Heversham/Milnthorpe Parish Register about 40% of all deaths were of children. In 1803 17 children died of convulsions, six of worms, four of 'teeth', one of the 'decline' and one of 'water in ye brain'.

Fecundity, toil and toughness were the main characteristics of the most important group of Westmorland farming folk. They were the Statesmen who elsewhere are called Yeomen, the traditional backbone of old England. Occupying what they held to be their own land they were beholden to no man. Indeed the spirit of independence went with them to the grave and the 1811 epitaph to John Robinson Hunter of Dovengill, one of the last Ravenstonedale statesmen, concluded 'He liv'd and died unplac'd, unpension'd, no man's heir and no man's slave'.

In a similar vein William Wordsworth wrote of the peasant republics of the Lakeland valleys where the tillers of the soil ruled the earth around them. Most statesmen had, however, a nominal overlord to whom 'customary' rent had to be paid. 'Inland' holdings as distinct from the wide open fells were invariably small and most were between 20 and 10 acres though many were less. In 1541 out of 187 holdings under Lord Wharton in Ravenstonedale 138 consisted of less than 7 acres. More often a statesman with a freeholding would also rent some more 'in land' as well as having stints on the fells. Thus in 1699 John Pearson of the Lyth Valley left to his grandson his estate at 'Powbank (Pool Bank) of Lord Richard Earle of Derby, at Rent 13/5...and 2 closes Arrable and Pasture ground bought of James Rowlandson...being ffree land'. Next year from nearby Brigsteer Richard Collinson left 'Houses, Peate Moss, Catell gates, common rights' for sale to be divided amongst his heirs. Rents, of course, varied in accordance with the variety of the County's land. In the 1790's a hay meadow in Troutbeck was let for 50s per acre while in the south, near Milnthorpe, field rents were £4 per acre and they could be a pound dearer around Kirkby Lonsdale.

Despite the huge preponderance of open moorland Westmorland was in fact a county of ancient enclosure. Archaeology shows that some enclosures go back 2500 years to the Iron Age but from Medieval times the process was legally recorded. Walter Strickland in the fourteenth century was permitted, for instance, to enclose land near Sizergh 'except at Brigsteer which shall remain unenclosed except where (already?) enclosed'. In northern England some enclosure was essential, especially in hilly areas, where there were not compact stretches of arable land large enough for a whole community to work together

'Flustering sheep' - from summer to winter pastures, Kendal c.1954
Photo: Margaret Duff Collection

which was possible in the flatter grain growing lands of the South and Midlands. In Westmorland patches of plough land were as scattered as were the people. Nuclear villages with cottages and gardens - the crofts and tofts - clustered around a village green occurred mainly in North Westmorland especially in Eden. Elsewhere, as for instance in Witherslack in South Westmorland, little groups of farmsteads could straggle for several miles down a valley without there being any obvious village centre. Individual statesmen might farm a sprinkling of detached fields varying in size and description. Thus John Cragg's 'estate' of less than 30 acres at Ackenthwaite when purchased by John Smyth in 1742 was split into seven separate holdings named respectively 'Brunthwaite, The Parrock or Cragg Parrock, The Close called The Pickle, Holdings Hill, Gaudy Bank, Law Close and High Close'. When John Chambers bought a similar estate nearby in 1746 it consisted of 13 separate crofts and closes including Marsh Close a couple of miles away on the Heversham mosses. The latter was a typical feature of this area's agriculture which, incidentally, persisted throughout the next two centuries, whereby 'hardland' away from the marshes was farmed at the same time as tidal flats and mosses known as 'soft' land which were used for grazing. Such an arrangement involved the seasonal movement of stock, a practice known as transhumance. To facilitate quick movement rough tracks connecting differing types of land were allocated. One of these, called Fluster Gap, surviving at Heversham, was where sheep and cattle were driven from off the marsh onto the higher safety of Heversham Head. In Lunesdale and Lakeland the swards connecting valley tofts with the fells were called outgangs.

Fells and other commons invariably belonged to the lords of the manor who might be absentee grandees with little interest in the local people as long as they paid their stints. More often the landlord, or his steward, was directly involved with farming the fells for they owned the tenant's stock as well as his land. The custom probably went back to the Middle Ages when, for example, the Abbot

of Furness provided his Lakeland fiefs with sheep for their grazing grounds or 'wicks', 'cotes' or 'folds'. When Henry VIII confiscated the Abbey's property in 1537 its 'Herdwyks and shepecots' were valued at £39 13s 4d. Therefore, it was the 'wick' form of land tenure that gave its name to the Herdwick sheep which became Westmorland's most famous animal, whose head forms the crest on the county's coat of arms and

Cumbria coat of arms
crested by a Herdwick tup

also on those of the new County of Cumbria. By the 1700's the practice of letting land and sheep together was closely regulated. When Robert Philipson of Ashes, Staveley, near Kendal, let his estate at Over End and under the Tongue, in Kentmere, to John Godman he included '80 Heaff Bred and Heafe Going sheep'. At the end of the lease 'the tenant (has) to deliver to the landlord 710 Loads of Manure, at the expiration of his Farm...and to redeliver 80 heaf sheep of the like number, sorts and kinds and in such plight and condition in every respect to the judgement of four persons to be indifferently chosen.'

Always living within sight of the fells where they had 'heaf' rights Westmorland's townsfolk like their country cousins were involved in agriculture as well as in trade. Often deeds for a town's cultivatable lands are more detailed than for rural transactions. In 1577 Allan Bellingham of Levens bought in Kendal 20 tofts, 10 barns, 12 orchards, 20 acres of (arable) land, 10 acres of meadow and 20 acres of pasture and common pasture.

Kendal and the county's other market towns and larger villages did have some open field cultivation. On Speed's Map of Kendal of c. 1611 a plough team is depicted on the town's open field at Mintsfeet. Kendal's open fields (amounting only to 105 acres) and also those at Kirkby Stephen, Bolton and Soulby in the north of the county were enclosed around the turn of the eighteenth century. Some persisted for much longer. Thus Neddy Stones in 1917 recalled that his mother, perhaps in c. 1820, had worked in Milnthorpe's open fields - on what became Dallam Park - 'and used to lead the plough horses, a customary matter in the common sense days of old'.

In South Westmorland and the Eden Valley there were tenant farms of over 100 acres of arable and good 'in-land'. Even so Pringle found that 'tenanted farms (are) so small that a rent of £100..(is).. rare; tenure is often short as little as 4 or 5 years but most about 8 or 9'. Already a complex pattern of dates set for transferring farms was coming in. In North Westmorland most of the holding was taken on Candlemas Day (2nd February). In Kentdale the arable land was taken on the 14th February, pasture etc. on the 5th April and the buildings and farmhouse on 12th May.

Around 1799 Statesman's farms, once the most typical form of land tenure in Westmorland, were beginning to decline for the age of large capitalised tenant farms typical of the nineteenth and most of the twentieth centuries was dawning. It was the bigger tenants like several members of the Ellison and Handley families who dominated the Kendal Agricultural Society and its shows for the first century of its existence. A few descendants of the Statesmen like the Willisons of the Lyth Valley and the Atkinsons of Farleton retained their independence though neither their status as farmers nor their agricultural achievements as measured by prizes awarded at the show were any better than those of top tenant farmers.

Despite the persistence of some Statesmen Wordsworth in 1830 was already lamenting 'the disappearance of the yeoman class as one of the most important and tragic events' of his early years. He also believed that the process had begun as early as 1770 and - erroneously - that it had been completed by 1820. Rural depopulation may have started even earlier in some areas. At Great Asby the number of inhabitants went down 10% from 388 in 1787 to 357 in 1801. More drastically - at least for the parson - the tithe of corn had dropped in Asby by nine-tenths because, it was claimed, 'of the decline in Statesmen's estates'.

The alleged decline of Statesmen did not necessarily mean a corresponding decline in other forms of agricultural labour. There were mixed opinions about changing working patterns in the 1790's. In South Westmorland, even when there was a large working family, farmers with less than 100 acres would still hire labour. On the other hand Pringle, referring mainly to Lakeland and the eastern hills, pronounced that 'wages are dearer than in any neighbouring county on account of there being so many smaller proprietors (which) has led to a general disinclination to labour for other people'. He instanced that an experienced male farm servant - known as a 'hind' - ' may be employed by the year at £20 with house, garden and potato ground; unmarried at 12 guineas with washing'. Casual labour rates included 'Day labourers at 1s 4d to 1s 8d; monthly at £1 12 6d....Harvesters 9s to 10s per acre by the sickle - the scythe not being used in the reaping of any sort of grain. Hay 2s 6d-3s 6d-a man can mow an acre a day. Moal Catcher 3d an acre first time; 2d acre thereafter.' Farm wages in fact seem to have risen markedly over the previous 130 years although it was a period of low inflation for in 1667 the Kendal Magistrates had fixed rates of pay at: 'The Chief hind, by the year £2 6s 8d; The inferior Hind...£1 6s 8d; Boy for driving plough for the year 13s 4d; Hedgers, ditchers and all other common labourers, the harvest excepted, with meat 1d, without 4d per day'.

'Meat' was but a generative term for 'board wages'. Indeed the carnivorous element in the diet was always meagre and varied in accordance with the season as well as with the prosperity of the household. Up until the middle of the eighteenth century 'meat was not eaten except at Christmas and Easter but farmers lived on bread and butter and whatever little matters the farm could afford'. Sparsity of meat was due to the lack of winter forage which meant that most stock had to be slaughtered in the autumn.

Meat fairs and markets were a major feature of the farming year and, as such, constitute part of the ancestry of Agricultural Shows. A 'direct ancestor' of Kendal Show was the 'Back End Fair' held on, or about, the 8th and 9th of November on Beasts Bank which served much of southern Lakeland equivalent to the later 'Show District'. In 1791, shortly after the butchers row of shops in the Old Shambles was erected, bull baiting was abolished in Kendal but the practice continued until 1820 in Appleby and 1824 in Kirkby Stephen. Penrith market served North Westmorland and in 1690 they 'killed 300-400 beasts every day.' At the other end of the county at the Martinmass Market at Burton-in-Kendal in c.1750 over 80 pigs in a day were sold at the give away price of a 'farthing in the pound for immediate salting'. Even though salt, in vast quantities, was imported through Milnthorpe there was rarely enough for all the required 'salting' and so much of the Autumn killed meat was merely pickled in brine where it soon went off. Smoking was often more effective for both mutton and hams and there were smoking lofts up the cavernous chimneys of the 'fire houses' in the bigger farm houses. At one farm in 1787 Clarke saw seven sheep hanging by their hind legs in one chimney. Westmorland ham was a far famed delicacy. Hams were cured by being first rubbed with 'Bay salt, sometimes covered up, sometimes left on the bench. They were then rubbed with salt and salt petre, hung in chimneys to smoke either over peat or coals for anytime from a month to eight months when hams were packed in straw and sold to London, Lancaster or Liverpool'. Westmorland ham was sent to London at least as early as 1757 and in 1792 (when they were noted by Pringle) they were bringing 7d or more a pound.

By the 1790's times had changed and, Pringle asserted, the labourer was living as well as his employer had done 50 years earlier. He would consume for 'Breakfast milk pottage and bread and cheese; pint of ale in the forenoon and in the afternoon; dine on meat boiled baked, or roasted or potatoes and pudding; sup on cold meat'. Wheat bread was a rare luxury and in Patterdale and northern Lakeland it was served only at funerals when it was called 'arvel' bread. Most bread was made from oats called 'haver' or from barley - 'bigg' - or from a mixture of the two. The local name for it was 'clap bread' or 'clap cake' as its squashed cob form resembled a cow clap. Like the similar 'cakes' burnt by Alfred the Great the dough, having been rolled or patted out into discs about 22 inches in diameter, was placed on the hearth stone to rise before being baked - not in an oven but in the fire on a metal three legged stool called a girgle or brandreth. Later opinions varied as to its quality. E. Armitt reported that most of it was 'exceedingly black, coarse and harsh but...that oat clap bread was delicious'. Pringle estimated that 'a labouring man will eat 16lbs of meal made into bread in a fortnight at a medium cost of 2s. As the labourer had wages of 8s a week he would therefore have 6s for the remainder of his own sustenance and the sustenance of his family and the cloathing (sic) of them all'. Oat meal porridge was the staple dish in poorer households. At a slightly later date in Milnthorpe Workhouse, where the diet was supposed to mirror that of the labouring class, porridge was served at 17 out of 21 meals in the week. For variety it could be made with milk or water, and for treats it was flavoured with sugar or treacle when it was called 'hasty pudding'.

Though the well fed agriculturists of 1799 scoffed at the primitive practices and way of life of their forebears the array of substantial farmhouses, which are

Even a taste for 'Olde Worlde' charm does not hide the basic squalor of a smaller Statesman's farm, High Birk House, Little Langdale
From 'Some Westmorland Farmhouses'. 1945

23

the county's greatest architectural glory, testify to the prosperity of earlier centuries. The Royal Commission on Ancient Monuments of 1936 listed sixteenth- or seventeenth-century farmhouses in half the county's parishes. Some like Beetham Hall, Burneside Hall and Ormside Hall are really small fortresses with a Pele Tower at their heart. Helsington Laithes, Gaythorn and Hincaster Hall are small Elizabethan Manor Houses; so too is Townend, Troutbeck the ancient home of the Brownes though they are often described as statesmen. The masters of these houses whether they were independent squires or substantial tenants for a greater Lord would have farmed at least 100 acres and often much more. Representative examples of Statesmen's houses are plentiful and diverse and include Fellfoot, Langdale home of the Fletcher Flemmings, Flodder Hall Lyth - the Knipe family, Hackthorpe - one of the Lowther properties and Hollin Hall, Staveley seat of the Philipsons. On the borderline between Statesman's and the better type of peasant's croft are Glencoyne Farm, Patterdale, Drawwell, Lyth and Low Fold, Crook, all of which show signs of having grown out of a Medieval Long house where stock and people lived under the same roof though separated by a 'through passage'. Few of the humbler homes have survived. Most had been clumsily thrown together from field stone or from that 'taken from the quarry before the present art of cutting them was understood' (!) and as may be seen in illustrations in some of the early Tourist Guides many had thatched roofs.

Man and beast lived together in a shitty symbiosis. Everything and everybody would be contaminated with the stink and smear of filth oozing out of middens and shippons which coalesced with droppings from farmyard fowls and swine. Much of the clarty mess would then be clogged indoors and trampled into the miry rushes strewn on the floor. No one minded as 'Wha iver heard o'cow muck makin a body badly?' Even in the Statesman's hall stench and smoke oppressed the atmosphere. Sooty cobwebs known as 'the hallen drop' cast by the peat fire fell on the heads of all and may possibly explain why pictures of seventeenth century interiors show both men and women wearing hats or bonnets. Peat generally called turf was the main fuel for most of Westmorland though a little coal did come from Stainmore and Ingleton or was imported as sea coals through Milnthorpe. Peat cutting or turbary rights were, therefore, highly valued and their retention was a major impediment to improving the moors and mosses from which the fuel came.

A clear indication of the way of life and economic role of the middling rank of country people can be gained from inventories of homely articles, farm stock and equipment. On most farms implements were of only nominal value. Thomas Preston's tackle, in 1700, amounted to 'Cart and wheels 5/-, Harrow-barrow 2/6, Gavelock 1/-'. In 1707 the 'utensils' belonging to James Wilson of Beckhouses in Grayrigg consisted of 'Wheelwood, Cheese press and wood 5/-, Carts and

Wheels £1. 0. 0., Saddle and bridles 5/-, Ploughs and Ploughgear 10/-'. By later standards carts were small, no doubt because of the narrow lanes, being according to Pringle 52 inches wide, 36 inches long and 14 inches deep. Ploughs were 'light not neatly constructed, some have a wheel at the extremity of the beam to keep the furrow at an equal depth'. Oxen were still used in the 1700's and an 'oxe-yoak' appears, along with '4 pack saddles, 5 pairs of holts and a peat holt', in the inventory of William Hawkrigg of Underhelm, Grasmere. Though horses were common enough they were small and of little value being probably little better than the wild fell ponies that still roamed the moors round Kirkby Stephen, Brampton and Kentmere. These were described as 'miserable looking creatures, with their long thick coats...always black, brown or grey never chestnut'. Thoroughbreds were unknown except, possibly, in the stables at Dallam Tower, Levens Hall and Appleby and Lowther Castles. Statesman John Pearson's horse power at Powbank, in 1701, consisted of merely a gelding and two mares valued at £8. His neighbour Rowland Crosfield's stable was worth even less in 1707: 'Two Mares and one Filly £3. 0.'

Only the upper Georgian Squirearchy could aspire to the ease and sophistication of the age Chippendale and Hepplewhite. A more spartan existence for lesser landowners is revealed by inventories of their household goods which, though often itemised in detail, were sparse and of little value. In most estates clothing was worth more than furniture. Elizabeth Wright of 'Sidggwick' who died in 1729 clearly regarded her 'Apparell' as a major part of her estate although she was fairly well off being described as the owner of a 'Mantion or dwelling house'. Her bequests included 'to my cousin Agnes Harrison my best brown petty coat. My best say appron, my best searge under wastcoat, my best straw hat, my leckin bodies...To Margaret Jackson my brown half thick petty coat, the better of my little under coats, the worse of my under shifts, my worse say apron, my best hardon shift, my best shoes, my camlot Hood...' Similarly the 1707 will of Thomas Camm of Camsgill, Preston Patrick details the items in a Statesman's clothing 'chist': after leaving his granddaughter Anne a 'pair of blew curtains' and her sister Ellinor 'a feather bed I bought in John Jackson's sale' he disposed of his apparel to 'John my best Vest and Bretches and my Kane. To Edward my next best Vest and Bretches with my Seall. To my Son in Law John Moore my best Rideing Coat and my best Hatt. To my son John Audland my cloath Rideing coat...' In 1705 George Williamson of Bannerigge's 'Purse and Apparell were valued at £6. 6. 0.' while his furniture consisting of 'Bed stocks, Bed cloathes and sheets, Tables, Chestes, fformes, chayres and stools' came to £4. 14s with in addition £3. 6s for 'Brasse and Pewther, Girdle Brandiron and other Iron things, Wooden Vessell and Earthern pots' valued at £3. 6s. George was described as having been a Tanner but that he was clearly also a farmer is shown by a list of his farm stock: 'Hay and Corne £10. 0. 0. Meal Malt

£1. 10s. Wooll 18/-. Butter and Cheese and other Victuals £1. 3. 4... Beasts £8. 0. 0. One Colt £2. 0. 0. Sheep £1. 0. 0. Pultry 8d.' (!).

The low value of George's livestock reveals the small size of herds and flocks - let alone the poultry side of his husbandry - which corresponds to similar evidence in more exclusively agricultural estates. The estate of Thomas Moore (died 1718) of Sunnybank in 'Grayrigge' was one of the most valuable proved by probate in the early eighteenth century. Even so it only comprised 'Twenty two head of Beasts Young and Old £45. 0. 0. Two Mares and a Fillye £8. 0. 0. Sheep Young and Old £14. 0. 0. A hog 15/-. Fuel for ye Fire, Manure and Pultery £1. 0. 0. Stocks Hay, Bigge and Oats £23. 0. 0. Meal, Malt, Butter, Cheese and other Victuals £6. 0. 0.' George Dixon's flock was the biggest recorded at the time amounting to '120 Heave-going Sheep at ffell-foot in Little Langdale now by me lett to ffarm by Lease paroll to John Hodgeson'. No valuation was provided but he also owned 'Beasts £10.10. 0' and 'Sheep at Heaning' £5. 19. 0. Most farmers left less than £10 worth of cattle and £5 of sheep. Rowland Crosfield's flock at Witherslack was, indeed, only worth 18s in 1701. He also left 'One Cow £2. 0. 0. Two Mares and one Filly £3...and Honey and Bees £1. 10. 0.' Honey also appeared in the will of Thomas Camm who left to his granddaughters his warming pan and 'bed cloathes together with my stock of Bees to be equally divided'. Sadly history does not record how they managed to share out Thomas' bees equally between them, nor the degree of gratitude expressed by his grandson Edward on being bequeathed his granddad's 'next best vest'.

Fair shares for all descendants, though difficult to achieve, was a reasonable aspiration. Richard Atkinson of Farleton, however, attempted to rule his roost from beyond the grave as he stipulated in his will of 1717 that 'in case it shall happen that I dye after the second day of ye Month called February and before ye crop be got on the lands that then and in such Case my Executors shall not plow and sow more of ye said Lands in that year than I in my life time usually and ordinarily ploughed in one year'. Richard seems to have had his way for Farleton remained an important arable area especially for prized root crops and the William Atkinson Cup (named after a descendant) for general cultivation was the largest in size of any trophy awarded at the twentieth century shows.

Richard's will illustrates both the historical importance of arable and - yet again - the attachment of Westmorland farmers to tradition. Though ill suited to most cereals Westmorland from the earliest times had necessarily to produce its own bread stuff. As the names of Milburn, Milnthorpe and Milton show flour was ground all over the county from the earliest times. The recorded history of many villages virtually starts with a mention of a water mill. Kaker Mill at Preston Patrick was first mentioned in 1119 and is one of the earliest recorded mills in the country. Milnthorpe's mill(s) probably originated with the Danish-Norse settlers before 1000 AD. The first reference to a Milnthorpe mill occurs only in an award of Tithes to Heversham Church in 1460 but it included a copious list of the agricultural products of that time, for the parson was to receive: 'a third part of the Mill of Milnthorpe, anciently belonging to the said church, also the tithes of fishings,...foals, calves, pigs, brood geese, hens, ducks, bees, eggs, pigeons, lint, hemp, leeks, onions, and garden products of the whole parish'.

Flax and hemp for linen were still grown near Milnthorpe and also in the Eden Valley in the eighteenth century but the main concentration, as in all the lower lying areas, was on corn which even included wheat. 'From Milthrope to Burton and from Burton by Farleton to Kirkby Lonsdale farms and inclosures are larger. Some wheat is grown with a yield of 45 bushels per acre from 4 bushels of seed which had been previously prepared by soaking in brine or washed with chamberlye and dried with lime'. Oats and barley, the main cereals, were also the key elements in the arable rotation which started with 'land overgrown with moss' being ploughed in March and sown in April with oats yielding 60 bushel from seven and a half Winchester bushels of seed. For the second crop the land was ploughed soon after Candlemas (February 2nd) and fertilised with 100 cart loads of manure to the acre. It was then sown with 4 bushels of barley (called bigg) which generally yielded 54 bushels. The crop was oats sown after ploughing in April and harvested in September. The land was then left to itself producing a poor crop of hay in the first year and the best crop

A softer South Westmorland scene. Haymaking in Dallam Park c.1820

in the third. All this labour which became even harder and less productive the further the plough moved up on to the fells was not enough and Nicolson and Burn (like Camden 200 years earlier) recorded that there was 'not sufficient oats within the county'. Hence there were large markets for corn at the entrances to the county at Burton and Penrith.

Some changes had occurred. Potatoes were grown sufficiently plentifully in the hind's tofts and on oat stubble in Kentdale that a potato market was established in Kendal as early as the 1730's. Apart from onions few if any other vegetables were grown. Although orchards occur regularly in title deeds their fruit must have been just for home consumption and the 'Kendal damson' market, for instance, was not mentioned before 1799. By the 1790's turnips for winter feed (though produced in the south from the 1640's) had been introduced round Kendal and near Temple Sowerby in Eden but were more or less unheard of elsewhere.

The county's hide bound disparity was shown by the lack of standard units of measurement. Even Pringle got confused in reporting the county's weights and measures which 'vary from place to place and amongst commodities. The pound consists of 12, 16, 18, 20 or 21 lbs. Winchester bushels are three times greater than customary bushells and a bushell of two bushells is used for sale of potatoes at Appleby. Rye is sold by a boll of two bushells and potatoes by four and a half. Acres (vary) from statutory 4,840 square yards, customary at 6,760 and a third acre near Milnthorpe and Burton is 7,840.'

Improvements in stock and crops were bound to be slow because little was done to augment the fertility of the soil. In Westmorland, Pringle grumbled, the 'prejudice against artificial plants is almost universal'. Clover was hardly grown at all while hay grown from sown grass was held to be poorer than that 'made of the trash spontaneously by the land... Lime burning, using Stainmore or Ingleton coal as fuel, began in the east of the county in the first half of the eighteenth century but it was not until the early 1800's that lime from kilns peppering the South Westmorland plain contributed in a big way to the improvement of the existing cultivated land and to the clearance of fell wildernesses.

Bad as was the general state of arable cultivation in Westmorland before 1799 contemporaries reserved their worst comments for the county's stock. Westmorland ham won praise but the animals from which it came did not. William Ellison told a farmer's gathering at Milnthorpe in 1813 'that a few years ago the pigs had big ears and misshapen snouts, their ears so big as to cover their eyes nor were they blessed with fat'. Pringle also said that local swine were small though otherwise 'good' and did not comment on their appearance.

Sheep were another matter: 'they are horned dark or gray-faced, thick pelleted, with course, strong hairy wool'. Interestingly he did not once mention

A ram of the Heath breed

Herdwicks by name and instead reported that Westmorland flocks were composed mainly of 'the mountain breed either native or a cross with scotch rams.' Though no attempt had been made 'to improve their carcass or the fleece' he provided some information as to how they were reared. Only the wedders stayed on the tops as they alone were able 'to endure the severity of the storm or falls of snow and so are left to shift from themselves'. Even then their fate was chancy and, it was claimed, a third of all Westmorland's sheep died in the winter of 1793. Although they were salved (with a mixture produced 'from a gallon of tar and 16 lbs of butter') ten per cent of sheep wintered on the low lands died of diseases like 'the black water sickness.' Ewes, having dropped their lambs, were sent back to the fells after April 6th. The best sheep were a local breed the Silverdales which were white faced with close wool. In Burton and Holme they could 'yield a stone of wool at 8d a pound'. From the 1770's some of the new Lincolnshire breeds, as developed by the great Robert Bakewell, and also Leicester Cheviots had come

Robert Bakewell's new Leicesters c.1790

into the county but twenty years later they were still at the experimental stage. As for the Herdwick its nature was so imprecise that no two descriptions seem to agree while its physical makeup was so varied that some sheep had 14 ribs rather than the usual 13. In the 1880's an old timer reminiscing in 'The Field' said that at the turn of the century Herdwicks 'looked like the last remnants of barbarism with large manes and beards of very course hair. Noses were light grey and were then called raggy or rimy from its resemblance to hoar frost. After heavy rain the wool turned black as if drenched with soot water and was evidence of a severe check to thriving'. Apart from their legendary toughness Herdwicks were valued as good milkers.

This was a surprising attribute as Westmorland was already noted for its dairy cattle. Pringle even went so far as to claim that 'there are few counties...in which there is no great manufacturing town where more milch cows are kept'. But (confirming the evidence from statesmen's probates), he added 'the farmer keeps just such cows as he has bred and they by no means yield so much as would be expected from Dutch or even Scotch breeds'. A surprising amount of milk was sold for drinking and rather later, in 1836, there were 79 milk 'typlers' in Kendal though, regrettably, 71 of them were in trouble for giving short measure.

Westmorland was not a great cheese making county although cheese appeared, for instance, in the Kendal Market regulations and cheese presses occur in farm inventories. Instead most of the county's dairying was concentrated on butter production. 10 dairy cows, if grazed on good pasture, could yield 20 56 lb firkins of butter in the summer season. With some justice it was contended that the quality of Westmorland butter derived from 'the sweet and herby nature of its pastures rather than to the method of making it or the conditions under which it was kept'. Milk for creaming was 'stood' in wooden cisterns, though around 1800 metal (including lead!) and earthenware creamers were coming in. Churning was still done in the age old vertical up and down pole churn in dank shacks, sometimes doubling as calf sheds, utterly unlike the cool flagged, scrubbed and white washed dairies of a later date. Supplies could not keep pace with a growing demand and butter prices rose in Kendal from 3d a lb in 1737 to 6d a lb in 1777. Even reasonable milking cows were worth only about £8 in the 1770's and it would take a year for them to yield the same value in milk. Meat was still (in 1799) a much better option for the stock farmer. Indeed, harking back to the earliest times cattle for horns and hides as well as food had been the main source of wealth. Nout geld and the herriot tax levied before and after the Norman conquest had been assessed on the value of horned cattle. Like sheep 'wicks' cattle were let as part of land tenure when they were called 'gelts' or (tantalisingly for some ill informed investigators 'gold'(s).

Cattle markets and fairs also shaped the layout of some market towns and villages. Milnthorpe market was founded in 1334 as a Cattle Fair which continued to be held - on the 12th May - until 1929. Cattle rustling was a major Medieval pastime as in 1336 when Alexander de Wyndsoeur accused William de Courcy of 'detaining unjustly 8 oxen and 8 cows at Heversham in a place called Milnthorpe'. These beasts were probably of the long horned native breed, variants of which still held sway at the turn of the eighteenth century and indeed were still to be seen at shows until the 1840's. Pitt in 1809 praised their 'graceful curving horns, white back and brindled sides'; some also had a white 'finched' streak running down their backs. Though they looked good Longhorns were not as productive as other breeds which in the 1790's were coming in rapidly. Of these Scotch cattle like Argyleshires or Kyloes and especially black Galloways were the most prized. Being excellent feeders Black Cattle 'lay fat on their backs' and one beast at Lowther weighed 33 stone a quarter! At the end of September 10,000 Scotch beasts of all types and conditions were sold at Brough Hill Fair either for autumn slaughter or 'bringing on' for later sale to the growing markets of industrial Lancashire and Yorkshire. To facilitate the movement of drovers roads criss-crossed the county. Cattle 'brought on' in Westmorland were put out on poor land for keeping or were penned in the straw yard and were 'ready for the shambles in May'. When kept indoors they were rarely given bedding and lay hard on filthy cobbles. Heifers also were fattened on good ground at a cost, Pringle estimated, of £1.1s per head. Proportionately more calves than in later centuries were reared for veal which was popular in the Kendal area where it was sold in c.1790 at 5lb a pound compared to beef 3d-4d per lb. Inevitably disease was endemic in the foetid byres and there were catastrophic Cattle Plagues in 1745, 1757 and 1839. Though some farriers like the Audlands of Ackenthwaite tried their hands at veterinary medicine most breeders resorted to superstitious practices going back to Pagan times. As a talisman to the Devil or to cauterise disease bearing spirits, especially in the hoofs, cattle in spring were driven through a 'Need Fire'. After one herd had been 'treated' in this way a smouldering brand was retained to rekindle a fire in the next farmyard as the 'Need Angel' was not as effective in a new fire. As late as 1840 a Need Fire was taken in two days (!) from Crook to Levens and then to Crosthwaite and other places in the Lyth Valley before being taken out of Kentdale to the Howgills and thence to Lunesdale where it was last used in Kirk Lane outside Killington Church.

Except in plague years beef was the preferred meat and so other meat was much cheaper. At Kendal in Spring mutton was 7d a lb but it could be as low as 3d in the autumn but pork only varied from 3d to 4d per lb between the seasons.

Market prices for poultry are also available from the eighteenth century. 'Young Ducks apiece' sold at 4d and a goose at stubble' from 1s to 1s 6d in 1737. The respective 1777 prices were: ducks 10d, geese 1s 4d to 2s 6d. Twenty years later Pringle even quoted the price - at 3s/4s - for a turkey.

Though variety and numbers might have increased since George Williamson's 'pultry' was valued at 8d there was in this, as in every aspect of Westmorland agriculture, room for improvement. Happily the times were ripe for change. On the land as in the burgeoning mill towns the sleazy dawdle of centuries had stirred and was starting to accelerate into an economic revolution, the fastest and most drastic in our history. England was at war with Revolutionary France and to cope with the challenge of feeding a growing population and of paying for our own and our allies' forces the landed interests in Parliament had inaugurated a Board of Agriculture 'to fix the attention of a great nation on the improvement of its soil and so assist in the most ancient and important of all arts, that of providing food for man'. It was of course axiomatic that the Knights of the Shire and the Landed Lords, while boosting the nation's productivity would at the same time be feathering their own nests.

Specifically the landed interest pushed forward Parliamentary Acts of Enclosure as these enabled other improvements to be made. In Westmorland Bishop Watson enclosed 10,283 acres between 1760 and 1800. Already in 1787 a visitor to the county had noticed the results of the new 'spirit of industry': 'I know that there can be no more remarkable passages of the history of rural civilisation than the substitution of hedges for the rude metes and boundaries used in former times'. Such was his enthusiasm for improvement through enclosure that Pringle 'looked forward with emotion to the day when wastes will wave with valuable crops, bleat with profitable flocks or be cloathed in stately timber...what a noble field for exertion'. Carried away further he even envisaged botanical improvements that would acclimatise foreign exotics to Britain's temperate climate so that 'some thousand years hence, responding under their own olive trees, future Britons may quaff their own wine, or sip their own tea sweetened with the juice of their own sugar cane'.

Westmerians were more down to earth but, nonetheless, they too were affected by the temper of the times so that in the generation which straggled the end of the eighteenth and the start of the nineteenth centuries the county's agriculture was transformed by what (in later school history books at least) was called the Agricultural Revolution. Other agricultural revolutions followed. Indeed the greatest agricultural changes for Westmorland were possibly those sparked off by the demands of the Second World War. At that later time changes in crops, stock and land tenure partly eradicated the agrarian processes brought in 150 years earlier. Even so, though plants and animals might change, the most important element of life on the land has remained remarkably constant. This is, of course, the human element: for the descendants of the 'westmeringas' still farm their native pastures, fells and mosses.

The names of many of the farming families of Pringle's day and of much earlier crop up throughout the history of the County Show and are still with us.

Some go back to the Medieval roots of local recorded history. Before the fourteenth century surnames were rare and generally were either patronymics or place names. Thus a Levens deed granted certain lands 'saving the grantor's fishery of Kent, hart and hind and wild boar and sow' to Thomas de Beetham, Roger de Lancaster, Robert de Kerneforde (Carnforth), Alexander de Kirkeby, Alan de Pennington and, finally, to Benedict Gernet. 'Garnet' - in various spellings - is certainly one of the oldest of Westmorland's 'farming' names. In return for 'rendering a pair of white gloves' Gilbert the Constable granted Adam Gernet land and a mill at Viver near 'Hennecastre' in 1237. 150 years later one of the first inventories of Westmorland farming names resulted from tax returns called 'subsidies'. The Grasmere Subsidy of 1394 bore the names of Adam

'A show family', Mary Garnett 1742 - 1831 of Sizergh. Wife and mother of some of the exhibitors of the first shows.

Mary Garnett's direct descendant John Garnett of Ackenthwaite with champion Holstein, Milnthorpe Athabaska Arnside at County Show 1995. Photo: Westmorland Gazette

Jonsona, John Dykson, John Grysdale, John Doble (Dobie?), John Brigge, John Bank(s), William Ellotson and William Bakester. The Windermere subsidy along with more Rowlandsons included William Docker, John Dawson and William Frereson. Crosthwaite's subsidy included Mabel Knype, John Dawson, Matilda Hardye, Ralph Gylson, Thomas Hodgson and Robert Philipson. Other records add to the pattern of 'Show' names: in 1332 Thomas Cragg owed Symon Ryge 30s; in 1375 John son of William Forster of Beetham killed Alan Procteur at Dent, while an inquest at Burton in 1440 heard evidence from a host of Garnetts, Holmes, Prestons, Crofts, Atkinsons and Batemans. Around the same time at Preston Patrick and Preston Richard Robert Croudson (Crewdson) and Chubertus Scoticus (Cuthbert Scot) held land on or near the later show ground at Lanes Farm. Also in the fifteenth century the manors of Casterton and Kirkby Lonsdale yielded the names of Barnes and Baines, Bindloss, Dodgson, Jackson, Witton, Houghton, Watson, Moor, Gibson and Postlethwaite. Fast forwarding into Tudor Kentdale the tally of landholders bound to serve Walter Strickland 'with horse bill or bowe' in 1543 included John Nelson, James Saul, Edward Moon and Myles Parke. Seventeenth century Hearth Tax returns replicate these names while adding others like Sisson, Burrow, Stott and Mason. Since then, though some families have declined or even disappeared, the general succession of named and inter-related tillers and guardians of the Westmorland soil has hardly been broken. Significantly, from the Medieval to the modern age the most common of all Westmorland names is that derived from the same nominative source: 'Son of William'. Four men with that surname appear on the Witherslack Court Roll in the 1400's. A century later their descendants were still farming in Kentdale and in the Lyth and Winster valleys but one family had already altered the name to Willison. Happily and historically these names and the farming families that bear them flourish yet. By all criteria, however, the senior branch of the descendants of the 'Sons of William' are the Dallam Tower Wilsons.

At their head in 1799 was Daniel Wilson, one of Westmorland's leading 'agricultural improvers'. With lasting effect - at any rate for the next 200 years - it was Daniel and his associates who so enthused the Squires, Statesmen and tenant farmers of South Westmorland with that 'spirit of industry' that they shook off the die hard shackles of former times to get on with the 'new farming'. As part of the same revolution Westmorland farmers had to overcome their inbred bashfulness at coming forward in order to exhibit their recent achievements while demonstrating their high hopes for the future. Out of their enterprise and courage was born The Kendal Show.

Above right: *Probably the oldest surviving show trophy 1807*

CHAPTER TWO

The Best and Worst of Times 1799-1839

1799 was a bad year - for Britain and for Westmorland. Politically any exuberance that had greeted the French Revolution had evaporated in a decade of massacre and war. British red coats had been driven from the continent by General Bonaparte's forces while at sea Nelson had not yet won supreme control.

Economically it was the best and worst of times. Driven by the Industrial Revolution at its fullest force the mill towns on the coal fields to the south of the county prospered as never before. Factory hands needed bread and with continental corn cut off by the naval blockade and with high tariffs to protect home grain from the scanty foreign produce Britain's rapidly modernising agriculture was doing well enough. Inevitably the diminishing in the supply of overseas corn at a time of increasing population led to a rise in agricultural prices. Between 1794 and 1800 the price of wheat rose from 44s 7d a quarter to the extraordinary level of 142s 10d. Though along with all members of the governing class the spectre of being murdered by a bread hungry mob was an ever present fear the late 1790's should have been a boon time for farmers. But in Westmorland there was a set back.

The problem was the perennial one - the weather. Historically the winter of 1798-1799 ranks with those of 1947 and 1963 as amongst the coldest ever. Snow smothered the land for four months on end and when the thaw came the skins of 10,000 lambs which had perished in the blizzards were sold in Kendal. Summer was no better. The 1790's saw the biggest fluctuations in rainfall on record. Kendal had 83 inches of rain in 1792 but only 46 in 1796. 1798 was drier with 54 inches but with typical perversity it rained at the wrong times. Writing in October from 'Calgarth, Kendal,' (*sic*), Richard Watson, Bishop of Llandaff was compelled to refuse an invitation to stay with the Duke of Grafton as 'we are now in the middle of harvest and the hay is not yet in...We have a more

Richard Watson, Bishop of Llandaff

determined season of rainy weather in this county than in most parts of England...so that we have had twice as much rain in the summer as in the spring months'.

A more positive reason for the Bishop's remaining in Westmorland may have been that he was currently engaged in the foundation of the Kendal Agricultural Society. His renown in developing Calgarth combined with his wider pre-eminence as a long serving member of the House of Lords had led him to be appointed to the first Board of Agriculture which in 1799 was currently involved in setting up experimental farms. These the Bishop argued, in a letter to the President of the Board, would be of little value because of the diversity of land and farming practice. Most of the improvements of the previous 50 years, he believed, had been induced by actions taken by nobility and gentry locally. It was their example which encouraged lesser land holders to copy the latest techniques and partake in future developments. Experimental farms were likely to be too distant for most farmers to visit while any learned publications resulting from the experiments might be equally beyond the grasp of the humbler farmers. Hence a locally based agricultural society which would organise exhibitions of farm produce from the farmers' own area would have greater educational value.

No one was better placed than Richard Watson to be in the forefront of the new movement. Personally he was at the centre of the web of Westmorland landed gentry interconnected through kinship and patronage and, moreover, he had the strongest links with leading agriculturists beyond the county. Because of the key role he played Richard Watson more than anyone else can be hailed as the principal architect of the Kendal Society and consequently of the Westmorland County Show.

Although he was a cleric and an academic and his father Thomas Watson had been headmaster of Heversham Grammar School he also came of landed stock. Indeed Thomas was able to leave the young Richard a legacy of £300 (worth perhaps £300,000 in the values of two centuries later) drawn partly from a family estate at Shap. While still at Cambridge Richard made valuable contacts with three dukes, Grafton, Rutland and Manchester, all of whom had estates in the south east where the Agricultural Revolution was being spearheaded by Coke of Holkham. Amongst the northern nobility the Bishop knew the Wyndhams who were Earls of Egremont, the Lowthers, Earls of Lonsdale and the Curwens of Whitehaven and Belle Isle, Windermere who also were leading agriculturists. More importantly for the emerging Kendal Society the Bishop's wife Dorothy was the sister of Daniel Wilson of Dallam Tower, the most pre-eminent South Westmorland squire of his day. Daniel, thanks partly to a large dowry brought by his wife an Egerton from Tatton Park, Cheshire, had enlarged and modernised his inherited lands around the Kent estuary. Currently he was engaged in driving through Parliament the Heversham Enclosure Act (passed in 1804) which transformed several thousand acres of mosses into mainly arable land and pasture some of which was grazed by his herd of black Galloway cattle. Two of the outlying shelters he built for the Galloways along with a block of model farm buildings designed for him by Webster of Kendal are still standing 200 years later. Like all farmers the 'old squire' suffered the odd disaster and in 1823 it was reported that 'a cow belonging to Daniel Wilson esq., at Dallam Tower ailing for some time was discovered on being opened up to have had in its stomach the skeleton of a leveret which it had swallowed'.

Accidents apart it was fitting that, at the probable instigation of his brother-in-law the Bishop, Daniel Wilson agreed to become the first President of the Kendal Agricultural Society. His patronage encouraged support from the cadet branches of the Wilson family like Christopher Wilson from Rigmaden, Kirkby Lonsdale and Abbot Hall, Kendal while the long serving treasurer of the Society Col. Thomas Holme Maude of Stricklandgate, Kendal, was Daniel's nephew. Other members of Kendal's commercial and land owning class who were early members of the Society were John Wakefield of Sedgwick, the manufacturer Jos. Braithwaite and Arthur Shepherd of Shaw End. Supporters amongst the Clergy included the Rev. Dr. Hudson the vicar of Kendal who also farmed the Haverbrack estate close to Dallam Tower and the Rev. Dr. Lawson vicar of Heversham who eventually bankrupted himself in an attempt to farm newly

Daniel Wilson, first President of the Kendal Agricultural Society

enclosed lands on Heversham marsh. Dr Lawson's failure led to a bitter quarrel with the owner of Levens Hall the Hon. Mrs Howard and his connection with the Society may be a reason why the Howards do not appear in the admittedly sparse records of leading gentry who attended the early shows. Nevertheless both Mrs Howard and her husband the Hon. Fulk Greville Howard were among the first 64 patrons of the Society along with 5 clergy, 22 esquires, 30 Mr's, two justices, two Colonels and the Earl of Lonsdale, Viscount Lowther MP and the Hon. H.C. Lowther MP. Kendal's nearest major landowners the Stricklands of Sizergh Castle do not seem to have taken an active part in the Society during its earliest years although their tenants William Ellison of Low Sizergh and the Garnets of Helsington were most successful exhibitors. Leading early supporters amongst Daniel Wilson's tenants included John Atkinson and his successor at Heversham Hall Obadiah Burrow, Alexander Webster of Ackenthwaite and R. Dennison of Beetham Hall. Landlords and tenants competed together in the various classes and during the 1820's Mr Moore the Squire of the Grimeshill estate at Middleton in the Lune Valley was often beaten by his tenants Mr Alan Kirk of Hawking Hall and Mr Richard Bowness of Middleton Hall.

The Society and Show also benefited from the active support of the Corporation of Kendal and significantly its first secretary William Briggs M.D. was Mayor in 1800-1801. As Kendal was the market town for all of South Westmorland its travel to market zone became the district of the new society and, moreover, the town's marketing arrangements set the pattern for the first exhibitions. For later generations used to exhibitions and shows of all kinds it is difficult to grasp how novel was the concept of a 'show'. The only precedents and also the name of 'show' came from the 'shows' of corn and butchers meat displayed for sale at the special fairs held generally in the spring and autumn. These were scattered throughout the town. Thus the butchers autumn show was staged in Stricklandgate as well as in the Shambles, horses were trotted out on the New Road, meal and flour in the space under St George's Chapel fronting Stricklandgate, cattle and sheep were sold in the Market Place and Stramongate, pigs and geese 'tied to carts in the high end of Stramongate' with potatoes at 'the low end' while fruit for the October damson fair was displayed in Highgate. In March 1816 a new Spring cattle fair was first held on Beast Banks which inevitably became one of the main venues of the Society's 'exhibitions' but it took 40 years before the Society came round to the original idea of exhibiting all classes of stock on one show ground.

From the stand point of national history the Kendal Show is significant as it was one of the earliest to be founded. The Bath and Western Show began in 1777 and by 1799 there were some half dozen shows mainly in the south of England. The nearest show to Westmorland was the Manchester Show while until the Workington Show was founded in 1805 the only show to the north was the

Highland Show in Scotland! Even so it was not for another thirty years that any other show was founded within easy travelling distance of Kendal.

It seems that The Kendal Agricultural Society was formed officially in August 1799 two months before it held its first 'exhibition', on the 19th October. The underlying objects of the Society were the 'improvement of agriculture within the County by promoting shows and offering prizes for the best in every branch of husbandry'.

Trophy and inscription for the best acre of grass, 1811

The rules of the Society were:

I   That the district of the Society be limited to the Wards of Kendal and Lonsdale.

II   That the annual subscription be not less than 5s or more than a guinea, but that larger sums be accepted as casual benefactions.

III   That the subscribers have two meetings annually on the days appointed for showing livestock.

IV   That all animals which have been bred on or after the 1st of January in any year be allowed to be shown as yearlings at any time the following year, and that the same mode of reckoning be applied to animals of any specified age.

V   That when a prize is offered for an animal, without expressing that it should be in the hands of the breeder, it be invariably required that such an animal shall have been eleven calendar months, at least, in the hands of the person to whom it may belong at the time of showing.

VI   That any person residing within the district be admitted a candidate for the prizes offered for lifestock; but that no one be allowed to claim any premium for the husbandry or crops on land of which he is the proprietor.

VII   That all matches and sweepstakes, entered into at the meetings of this Society, be inserted in the minutes, and be decided by the committee, in the same manner as the prizes offered by the Society; and that where premises are to be viewed for any wager, the parties shall give the same notice which is required from candidates for prizes for similar objects.

VIII   That seven subscribers be a quorum to transact any ordinary business; but that no existing law be altered except at a meeting where 20 subscribers are present.

IX   That any person obtaining a prize for the best general stock of horned cattle shall not have a second prize in the same account within a shorter period than five years.

X   That turnips succeeding potatoes, or any other sown crop, shall not be entitled to any prize.

Over the years the rules were modified and increased. In 1801 it was added that 'the bulls to be shown on the Saturday before Millthrop Fair; the heifers on the first Saturday in October'. Although all stock was on show either on the Beast Banks common or in the open streets there were no safety regulations until 1822 when it was resolved that 'no bull be shown in future without being rung at the nose and held by a cord'. Strict rules were laid down about crop inspections in 1803. Grass and general husbandry were to be inspected on the 24th June; barley on or before August 20th; turnips and livestock in the last week in September; rams and heifers to be shown in Stramongate on Saturday 6th October, at 11 o'clock. Inspectors were to be allowed expenses of 5s a day which, even allowing for inflation, was little enough in

Cup awarded to James Garnett of Hale Slack for the best two statute acres of grass 1821

view of the long distances to be travelled on horseback at a rate of rarely more than 6 mph. The slowness of travel meant that when, for instance, Mr Willison of Underbarrow in the Lyth Valley went over to the Lune Valley to inspect Mr Bowness' stock at Middleton Hall 25 miles away he would have to stay overnight. Consequently inspectors could find themselves neglecting their own farms for days on end. Although the improvement in roads over the previous half century had made it possible for farmers from a wide area to assemble, considerable difficulties remained especially in transporting livestock such as prized bulls or five sheep. To what extent stock were driven on the hoof or were carried in carts is not known but in any event 'going to the show' and 'coming back again' especially if the heavy dinner had been quenched would have been a tedious and time consuming task. Nevertheless, it was decided in 1825 to extend the Society's district to beyond the Kendal and Lonsdale wards and open the sheep and cattle classes to all members who had subscribed to the Society six months previously. Six years later in a magnanimous gesture William Ellison, who in both stock and crops had beaten most of the farmers in the immediate area, secured support for extending the district to include all the County of Westmorland and to within thirty miles of Kendal. Henceforward many exhibitors came from Furness, from the Lancashire part of Lunesdale between Whittington and Lancaster and from Sedbergh, Dent and Bentham in Yorkshire. Together with the county the area comprised a district larger than that of any other show until the advent of the Great Yorkshire, the Royal Lancashire and the Royal Show itself.

Rules concerning judging were progressively modified. At first all 30 members of the committee acted as judges; then in 1825 the number was reduced to 15. At the spring show of 1837 five judges only were selected to judge the bulls and stallions while at the autumn show it was decided to reduce the number to three for each class. If there was a disagreement the prize would be withheld 'which not infrequently occurred'. A novel solution to a dispute was, however, made at the 1838 show.

A big row had resulted at the dinner when Obadiah Burrow of Heversham Hall alleged that the winning short horn heifer had too many broad teeth for a two year old. Whereupon the winning owner Mr Morton of Skelsmergh Hall angrily asserted that that was no criterion to judge by and he and his brother were prepared to furnish proof. Eventually George Wilson of Dallam Tower, who was presiding, managed to streamline 'the debate' into whether to set up a panel to re-judge the animal and/or its class again or simply to vote there and then. After more furore the matter was put to the vote and Mr Morton won but Obadiah Burrow was not the only person present left wondering whether the method chosen was the best way to judge the quality of stock.

The actual organisation of the Society seems to have been haphazard by later standards. The only officers were the president, a post held by Daniel Wilson until a year or two before his death in 1827 when his place was taken by his son George Wilson, the treasurer who for most of the period was Col. Maude followed by John Wakefield and the secretary. All positions were unpaid and so it is not surprising that there was a steady turn over of secretaries. The first secretary Dr. Briggs was followed by another Kendal doctor Dr. Campbell who in 1811 offered a personal prize for the cultivation of turnips. About the same time he was replaced as secretary by William Gray M.A. Mr. Gray was the proprietor of a private school at Owlett Ash, Milnthorpe where he also farmed about 40 acres on which he grew several prize winning crops of barley. He was followed by two members of the same family W. and J. Lawson from 1821 to 1824 when they were replaced by Edward Tatham who served until the 1840's. As almost all documents and letters were hand written their task was onerous and unfortunately neither they nor most of their successors seem to have had sufficient time to ensure that any minutes, schedules or other records were safeguarded. Hence most of the 'hard' facts about the Society's early days have been culled from flimsy references in the Kendal Chronology and after 1818 by very brief and, incidentally, blurred micro-films of reports in the *Westmorland Gazette*. Much information about the Show quoted by Frank W. Garnett in his *Westmorland Agriculture 1800-1900* which was also summarised by Stephen Barratt in his pamphlet comes from a report of the reminiscences made by W. Longmire in an after dinner speech following the 1855 show. Hence only a general picture of the Society's earliest activities can be presented.

Until 1840 there were two shows, respectively in early May and late October both held on Saturday mornings and which were over by 2pm when dinner was served generally at The King's Arms in Stricklandgate. The first show was held in Stramongate which became the main centre for the autumn show while the spring shows were held on Beast Banks. From at least 1814 bulls and stallions were reserved for the spring meeting with other cattle and sheep being shown in the autumn. Only around 1816 did the Society provide sheep pens and previously perhaps the stock was tied to carts as was the custom at the meat fairs. From time to time sheep were also shown in Stramongate and for a decade from the late 1820's cattle classes were shown on the premises of T.H. and W.E. Maude behind Stricklandgate on what later became known as Maude's Meadow. Traditional arrangements seem to have broken down in 1839 when heifers, colts and fillies were tethered on Beast Banks while the sheep were hemmed into the Pack Horse yard 'a place which...is quite uncalculated for the exhibition and which has caused several of the farmers to demur from bringing their stock there again'.

Occasionally there were attempts to widen the shows' attractions. A prize was offered for pigs in 1805 and a three guinea cup presented by Daniel Wilson

Allan Kirk's cups for best managed farm 1810, best bull of any description 1821.

was won by Mr Jackson of the King's Arms in 1811 while, in 1815, another cup was offered for the best boar. That such encouragement paid off was perhaps demonstrated in 1819 when a pig weighing 65 stones was sold at Kirkby Lonsdale for £23! No long term classes resulted from a prize being offered for the best cottage garden in 1805 nor, twenty years later, when a cup was presented for a newly planted orchard to be awarded in the second season. Equally obscure was the result of a prize offered by John Wakefield in 1811 'for the industrious labourer who had brought up most children without recourse to Poor Relief' as the 'Local Chronology' explained 'we cannot discover to whom the amount of three guineas was paid'.

Most farmers preferred silver cups worth generally between 5 and 3 guineas as their prizes. Although up to a hundred cups and silver medals must have been awarded between 1799 and 1840 very few seem to have survived and despite an appeal for early prizes to be displayed at the Centenary Show in 1899 only one or two were discovered. Lucky exceptions are two cups won by Alan Kirk of Middleton respectively in 1810 and 1821 for the best managed farm and for the best bull. Amidst scores of trophies won by the Garnett family are early cups and ploughing match medals.

Because the need for bread and the obsession about the Corn Laws dominated the discourse of farmers even in a stock area like Westmorland the cultivation of the soil was the Society's top priority. As W. Longmire recalled in the early 1800's the argument went that 'if they improved the land they improved the stock but if their farms were not well tilled, well bred stock could not have justice done to them'. Significantly the first 'premiums' or official prizes were offered for crops and from 1810 the Society organised ploughing matches.

At the first ploughing match held at High Sizergh the best plough team of four men were given three guineas between them along with a single silver medal. In 1812 there were 14 entrants one of whom, it was widely reported, was using a Scotch iron plough. By 1825 there were 50 competitors at the match held at High Barns, Levens, most of whom were using iron ploughs made by E. Harling of Sedgwick. As many of the ploughmen did not rise to become farmers entering other of the shows' classes the lists of ploughing winners possibly

Above: *Inscription on probably the oldest surviving show trophy awarded to Chris Garnett of Low Sizergh for the best managed farm. 1807*

Below:
Trophy for the best managed farm, 1812

contain a greater span of local surnames. Thus the winners of the 1817 match were John Atkinson of Heversham Hall, John Cummings of Larkrigg, Alexander Webster of Ackenthwaite, Emanuel Westgarth of Cartmel Fell and John McKennie ploughman to Lieut. Col. Bolton. At the Sizergh ploughing match in February 1819 John Cummings of Larkrigg was again successful while his fellow winners were George Prickett of Mosside, Thomas Bathgate, Sizergh Fellside, William Pool, Barbon Beck Foot and Richard Willison of Underbarrow. 'In the evening the ploughmen, judges and others were regaled with good old English fare by Mr W. Ellison junior.' Altogether John Cummings won three ploughing

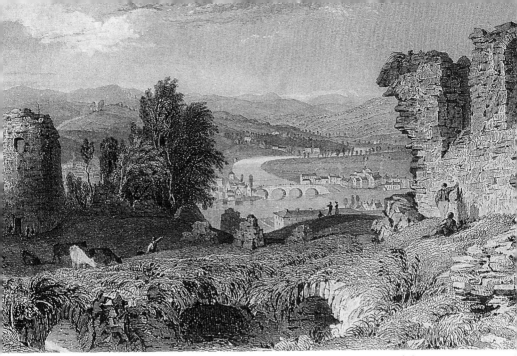

*Kendal from the castle c.1800 showing the undeveloped area east of the
River Kent where the show was later held*

competitions as did Richard Willison, William Simpson of Cinderbarrow and
John Barnes of Brigsteer but in his generation Alexander Webster was the
champion as he won four times.

There were two broad classes for cultivation, firstly for the general state of
a farm and secondly for individual crops. Early winners in the first category, for
which the award was a five guinea cup, were J. Jackson of Kendal in 1800,
William Dennison in 1801, William Ellison in 1819, William Pope? of Barbon
Beck in 1820, T. Gibson of Park End, Brigsteer in 1821 and W. Simm of
Watercrook in 1824. In 1825 the criteria for the farm management class were
spelled out as being 'for the tenant or occupier of any farm of not less than 40
statute acres who shall have the same in the best general cultivation, and in the
neatest and best order as regards to fences, drains, farmyard, cleanliness from
weeds, and in the most eligible and approved succession of green and white
crops'. William Ellison won the cup in that year and in several subsequent years
though he was beaten by John Wills of Lane End in 1826, by Bryan Holme of
Ninezergh in 1831, Henry Cottam of High Foulshaw in 1832, Obadiah Burrow
of Heversham Hall in 1836, Thomas Scott of Farleton in 1837 and W. Wilson of
Raines Hall in 1839. A special prize of £50 was awarded in 1820 to William
Ellison by the Board of Agriculture which offered a further prize of £25 for 1821.
Unfortunately the prize was never awarded as the Board was abolished as a
result of a government economy campaign.

'Turnip' cup 1816 awarded to
Christopher Garnett

Report of 1817 show and 'Plowing Competition'

Thomas Holme Maude, Efq. TREASURER.

William Gray, M. A. SECRETARY.

━━━━━━━━━━━●|❦|●━━━━━━━━━━━

At a General Meeting of the Subscribers, on Saturday, May 10, 1817,

DANIEL WILSON, Esq. President, in the Chair.

The SILVER CUPS were adjudged as follows:

1. To *Mr. Alan Kirk*, of Middleton for the best yearling long-horned *Bull*, in the Hands of the Breeder.

2. To Mr. Thomas Thompson, of Farleton, for the best *Bull* of any description.

3. For the best *Stallion* for Draught, or Husbandry Work.—To Mr. William Wilkinson, of Stalming, for his Horse Plough Boy.

4. For the best *Stallion* for the road or field.—To Messrs. Richard Raby, and John Dickinson, of Pilling, for their Horse Ishmael.

The PREMIUMS for PLOWING were adjudged as follows:

1. A Silver Medal and three Guineas to Mr. John Atkinson, jun. of Heversham Hall.

2. To John Cummings, Son of Mr. Thomas Cummings, of Larkrigg

3. To Alexander Webster, of Ackenthwaite.

4. To Emanuel Westgarth, of Cartmel Fell.

5. To John Mc Kennie, Ploughman to Lieut. Col. Bolton.

Prizes of silver cups (and once only a cream jug valued 2 guineas presented by the Rev. Dr. Lawson in 1836) were awarded by the Society for roots and permanent grass required for cattle feed. From the start the leading members expounded the belief of Arthur Young that turnip cultivation for winter feed would obviate the need for the Martinmass slaughtering while Pringle found that in Westmorland sheep fed on turnips increased in weight and value from 4d to 6d per pound. As early as 1800 there were two classes for turnips when the prize for the best half acre went to William Ellison and for one acre to H. Yeats of Skelsmergh. In November 1801 John Wakefield won a prize for the best acre of potatoes. First and second prizes were offered for turnips from at least 1819 when William Ellison and Alexander Webster were the winners. Another regular winner was J. Faulder the hind for Bishop Watson's Calgarth farm who in 1816 produced 46 tons of turnips from one acre!

The Society was in the vanguard of agricultural organisations when it encouraged grass to be treated as a main cultivable crop. Prizes were offered from c.1799 but the earliest recorded winners in the grass classes are Christopher Garnett of Sizergh in 1811, Thomas Benson of Cinderbarrow in 1812 and R. Willison of Underbarrow in 1820. No prizes for grass were made in 1824 'owing to an error in the entry' while because of another dispute the class 'was not decided' in 1825. The following year W. Ellison won but the popularity of the class declined thereafter and there were only two candidates in 1837 when T. Wilson of Lane Head was the winner. Also in 1837 there was a prize for 'the heaviest turnip' which weighed 26 pounds but there were no entries for a new class for 'Sanfoia' for which Thomas Home Maude had offered, the previous year, a prize of one guinea.

No prizes seem to have been offered specifically for wheat or oats and presumably any of these crops being grown would be judged in the farm management class. The barley class seems to have been popular possibly because only a small area of crop was judged. When William Gray won with his barley in 1800 it was for a mere half acre of barley. Mr Gray persisted and redoubling his efforts he won, in 1819, with an acre of barley! Other successful barley growers were J. Fothergill of Hutton Roof in 1801 and A. Webster of Ackenthwaite in 1820. From the 1820's onwards the Society began to encourage new crops and at the 1837 dinner 'a display of turnips, beans on the stalk, clover, Italian rye grass etc. was shown and Mr Ellison suggested that a collection of seed from the various grasses of the district should be made'. In 1838 'after the cloth was drawn the table was adorned with a handsome dessert of turnips that had won prizes'. Selected varieties on view included Dales' Hybrid, Pomeranian, Red Top and Green Top. Though interesting in themselves such botanical novelties only served to emphasise that the Westmorland farmers' main preoccupation remained stock rearing.

It was for the display of livestock that the first show was held. In 1799 there were three classes for cattle and for sheep. Silver medals for sheep were awarded to Arthur Robinson of Kirkby Lonsdale for a fell ram; to Robert Dennison of Beetham for a lowland ram and to Joseph Faulder of Calgarth for a pair of lowland ewes. Regrettably the names of the winners of the cattle classes have been lost but at the spring show held on Beast Banks on the 10th May following silver cups were won by Richard Bowness of Middleton for a Long Horn yearling bull and to John Atkinson of Heversham Hall for a two year old Long Horn heifer. Always the most valuable medals and cups were awarded for cattle whose main classes were soon well established. There were also sweepstakes for new entries which were financed on the show day by entrants donating a fee which paid the prize and the judges' expenses. At the 1820 show, for instance, the prize was half a guinea for sweepstakes for short horn cows and heifers and for colts and fillies but the award for the best breeding sow was only 5s which was won by R. Thexton of Grayrigg. In 1822 there were 12 sweepstakes but the most subscribers for an individual class was seven for gimmer lambs.

The most intense competition was for the silver 'cattle cups'. Already at the 1801 spring show cups were presented respectively to C. Taylor of Middleton for a Long Horn bull, to J. Harrison of Low Field for a two year old bull, to G. Garnett of Greenhead for 'best bull of the Long Horn breed' and to R. Dennison for a two year old Long Horn heifer.

There were also several sections for groups of animals such as the best stock of store cattle and for three heifers and a 'president's cup for three cattle and for five cows' which in 1824 were won by A. Kirk of Hawking Hall. Right down to the 1830's Mr. Kirk continued to be a frequent winner for the multiple classes though in 1831 he was beaten for the store cattle trophy by John Garnett of Greenhead.

For the first twenty years the old Long Horn cattle reigned supreme but gradually the Shorthorns crept in to begin their 120 year long domination of the Westmorland meadows, markets and shows. Lord Lonsdale gave an impetus to the breed when he boosted the nascent Lowther herd by the purchase of a Short Horn bull for 272 guineas in 1810. The following year the Kendal Society's secretary Dr. Campbell appealed in the press for support for the committee in encouraging the breeding of cattle 'including Short Horns'. The Garnett family of Low Sizergh were among the first breeders of Champion Shorthorns. Their most famous cow which won in c.1815 weighed 69 stones 2 pounds and produced 9 stones 2 pounds of tallow. By 1820 James Harrison of Low Field, who won a special sweepstake with a beast 'bred by himself', William Ellison of Sizergh and the President himself Daniel Wilson had all started breeding Short Horns. The following year the same three breeders won with shorthorns, William Ellison winning with a heifer, James Harrison with six heifers and Mr.

A 'brindled' longhorn

Wilson with 'the best cow'. By 1823 William Ellison had thirteen entries in the Coates Guide for bulls and in 1831 he had 19 females. About the same time James Harrison paid £50 for an eight year old Shorthorn cow and T. Morton of Skelsmergh (whose herd was held to be the oldest after that of Lord Lonsdale) already had renowned herds. Other South Westmorland breeders included Thomas Scott of Greenhead, W.E. Maude of Holmescales, J. Todd of Grayrigg, R. Willison of Underbarrow, Richard Taylor of New House, James Kilner of Mansergh and from Lancashire T. Jackson of Borwick along with 'others too numerous to mention'. Shorthorns were given classes of their own at the 1824 show when the main prizes for females were scooped by A. Kirk and R. Bowness of Middleton. The best Shorthorn bulls were 'Surprise' out of 'Lionel' bred by W. Ellison and 'Symmetry' belonging to Jonathan Colling of Burneside Hall. Moreover the show report announced 'no Long Horn bulls were exhibited this time'.

The Long Horns, nevertheless, took nearly twenty years to disappear from the show pens. In 1826 when 'the shew of stock was large and several animals of great worth and beauty of symmetry were brought to the notice of the judges' one of the praised beasts was a Long Horn heifer belonging to Richard Bowness. That Shorthorns had not yet won the day was indicated by their being only two entrants for a half guinea prize for 'the best Short Horn bull of the improved Durham breed' both of whom withdrew. Two years later there were five Long Horn bulls shown compared to only three Short Horns. In 1831 a silver cup for the best Long Horn bull was won by Mr. W. Stockdale of Witherslack Hall but there were no entrants in 1836. The next year they were back again as it was reported that there were 'four Long Horned candidates' and in 1838 'the Long Horns met with much approbation and were all round pronounced excellent'. Because of foot and mouth disease the 1839 show was sparsely entered and attended and there were only two Long Horn heifers on show. Two Long Horns were also shown in 1840 but they were the last to appear at Kendal while the last shown locally appeared at Kirkby Lonsdale in 1844.

Although in the first forty years of the show's existence the most prestigious classes were already those for cattle slightly more evidence of the sheep sections has survived. But throughout this early period no significant development similar to the switch from Long Horn cattle to Short Horns occurred. Already in 1799 a movement towards developing sheep of the 'improved' breeds was apparent but in the late 1830's the 'old Fell breeds' were holding their own. Consequently the random show reports that have survived are more valuable as a source for showing who were the main sheep farmers rather than indicating important trends in breed development.

A fell ram belonging to Arthur Robinson of Kirkby Lonsdale was the champion sheep at the first show in 1799 but a silver medal was also won by Joseph Faulder with sheep bred from crossing the native breed with New Leicesters introduced by Bishop Watson in 1792. Twelve years on in 1811 William Ellison won with 'the best yearling ram, produced by a cross for the improvement of the fleece'. By that time there were two distinct sheep classes and in 1812 John Franklin of Forest Hall was reported as having won with a shearling ram of the fell breed and C. Garnett of Sizergh with a shearling ram of the improved breed. Other recorded successful fell sheep breeders were J. Cornthwaite and R. Bowness of Middleton who won in 1800, Richard Noble of Selside and Michael Mattinson of Longsleddale 1801 and again in 1826 and 1831, George Robinson of Staveley 1819, Richard Thexton of Grayrigg Foot 1822 and several other years down to 1837, J. Cragg of Grayrigg 1822, John Bracken of Firbank, William Kellett of Longsleddale 1825, 1829 and 1831 and John Herd of Cautley 1838. Breeders of the 'improved' variety tended inevitably to come from the lower lands of South Westmorland. They included John Wakefield who first won in 1801, W. Ellison 1819 and many subsequent years, C. Garnett of Sizergh 1822 et seq, John Scott of Sedgwick 1831, and J. Ellison of Sedgwick. Sweepstakes were particularly popular among the breeders of 'improved' sheep and there were five in 1825 when John Wakefield esq. was the most successful entrant. In 1839 it was reported that 'Mrs Kendal of Sellet Hall together with Mr Richard Willison of Underbarrow exhibited some very fine shearling tups of the white faced breed'. Sometimes, however, there were very few entrants and in 1831 there were only three competitors for the best ewe sweepstake which was won by Mr. Johnson of Sedgwick. By 1838 when J. Scott's

PATTERDALE

WILLIAM MOUNSEY:

Stroke over the fillets, J M on the far Side, stoved on the near ear, and under halved far.

JOHN TAYLOR, Bauld How, New Church:

A stroke across behind the hooks with wad, and a pop upon the shoulder, J T on the near side, and some on the far, stoved on the near ear, and folded on the far.

JOHN TAYLOR, Bauld How, New Church:

A stroke down the near lisk with red, and down the far with wad, J T on the near side, and twinters J T on the far, stoved on the far ear, and fold under-bitted the near.

Fell sheep markings from Shepherd's Guide 1819

*Two sheep by
W.T. Longmire
Leicester/Cheviot
crosses*
Courtesy Dr. John Satchell

'improved' ram won there were eight entrants and every indication that the Sheep classes had regained their support.

Horses which became the most spectacular class at later shows did not appear at the very first of the Society's exhibitions. A prize 'for the best stallion to serve in the District' was first offered in 1805 and in 1808 John Parkinson of Marton won a cup for the most useful stallion. Around 1814 two distinct classes for horses for 'draught and husbandry' and 'for road and field work' were introduced but the names of winners have not survived. There were also sweepstakes for fillies and foals. In 1824 it was reported that a two year old filly sweepstake had been won by C. Garnett and for foals by Joseph Braithwaite esq. The next year the best foal prize (of only 5s!) was won by Robert Willison but although there were three and four candidates respectively for the filly sweepstake and for a cup presented by Arthur Shepherd of Shaw End 'for the best three year old colt or filly in the hands of the breeder' they had to be left undecided as the entrants 'were too evenly matched'. A two year old colt 'Constable' belonging to Mr Shepherd was also withdrawn. Later in the day Mr Shepherd who presided at the dinner offered to 'present one of greater value to stimulate the men of Westmorland to emulate each other in improving the breed of this noble, generous and useful animal'. Arthur Shepherd continued to sponsor the horse classes and in 1836 presented a silver cup to the owner of the best colt or filly in the hands of the breeder and bred within the Kendal district, 'three to be exhibited otherwise the cup will not be awarded'. Happily the right numbers came up and Mrs Kendal of Sellett Hall was the lucky winner. (Significantly too for the wider history of the show this is the earliest extant record of a lady winner!) Other sponsors included a Mr. Carruthers who offered two guineas sweepstake for the best foal by his horse 'Grand Arabia' which was won by Jonathan Colling of Burneside Hall with the second prize of one guinea going to George Kendal of Hill, Narthwaite.

The ups and downs of the horse section illustrate the feeling in the 1830's that the Society and Shows were losing their appeal. Financially the Society was often on shaky ground especially after Daniel Wilson ceased to be actively involved in its affairs. At first the shows' expenses were only about £10 as cups and medals were mostly provided by sponsors. In 1801, for instance, it was announced with obvious satisfaction that there was a balance of £1 5s 8d. Costs, however, gradually rose to £24 in 1824. Moreover three medals and nine cups had been purchased for over £40 and there were deficits in subscriptions of £44! Fortunately matters were rectified after the show in 1825 'when a large party sat down to a very excellent Dinner at the King's Arms; the President of the Society George Wilson of Dallam Tower Esq. was in the chair. Amongst the company assembled were the Hon Col Lowther, Hon J. Upton, Thomas H. Maude, J. Wakefield esquires, and many other gentlemen friendly to the agricultural interests of the County. The subscriptions were liberal and there was every prospect of a full and agreeable meeting another year'.

The 'County set' were not always as keen on attending the show as they were in enjoying the dinner. In 1832 it was noted 'that the stock was of a superior description and excited the admiration of all present'. But 'owing to the County Sessions being held that day the number of spectators and friends of agriculture was not as numerous as it would have been'. Again in 1836 the *Westmorland Gazette* stated 'the Show was neither so numerous nor so good as on former occasions'. Yet again, however, the dinner was well attended, 'the company being both superior and respectable'. The first reference to bad weather spoiling the autumn show day came in 1837 though it was claimed 'that at no previous meeting had the show of cattle and sheep been better'. In 1838 'the day was exceptionally favourable for the exhibition and a large number of practical farmers and agricultural amateurs came to witness the proceedings of the meeting'. There was also a fine day for the 1839 show but the 'show of stock was not large'. Nevertheless many 'gentry...together with upwards of forty of the most intelligent and respectable farmers of the district partook of a substantial well served dinner at the King's Arms Hotel. The viands and the wine gave the greatest satisfaction and did high credit to the attention of Mr and Mrs Holmes'. The drinking of 'innumerable toasts' did not, however, deter the members from grappling with the Society's problems and it was decided to set up a committee led by two of its most successful members William Ellison and Richard Willison to revise the rules and reorganise the show.

Whatever hopes there were for the success of their local efforts the Kendal and District landowners and farmers were facing a national crisis: they appeared to be about to lose the protection and support of Parliament. An implied warning had first been made in outwardly encouraging remarks uttered at the 1826 show when several speakers concentrated on 'intimating to the hardworking and industrious farmer that there is yet a gleam burning for him on the horizon. From hints thrown out in the political world it does not appear that ministers even yet, although they may still be further bullied by the manufacturers, dare further tamper with the Corn Laws, and thus weaken the best natural defence of our country by throwing down the firmest props and laying waste the soundest bulwarks of national welfare and national policy'. Soon, however, the 1832 Parliamentary Reform Act transformed the political situation by increasing the power of urban and industrial interests over that of agriculture and the countryside. Therefore, as the Society approached its half centenary the Westmorland agricultural scene looked in pessimistic eyes as bleak as it had seemed to the founders in 1799. Fortunately farmers both nationally and locally had not lost all their clout and, as it turned out, their future over the next fifty years was to be tinged with gold.

CHAPTER THREE

Bread, Beef and Butter 1840-1898

T he hungry forties' was the name given to the fifth decade of the nineteenth century. For two million Irish peasants hit by the Potato Famine 'the Great Hunger' meant death from starvation. In Britain leaner times hit the new industrial towns when a million factory workers were thrown out of work by one of the first cyclical slumps in trade and the bursting of a financial bubble in investment in railways. With no dole there was only skin flint charity and Workhouse 'Poor Relief' to ease the lot of the destitute: and significantly it was just at this time that Dickens portrayed the starveling Oliver Twist - 'asking for more'.

Abroad seething unrest at length erupted into the 'Year of Revolutions' of 1848. But at home the British governing class had been more astute and had staved off the danger of unrest when times were bad and ensured that industrial wages could be low when times were good by inaugurating a policy of cheap food, the result of adopting the principals of what was called 'Free Trade'. By Acts of Parliament finalised in 1847 Britain abandoned almost all customs duties on imports which was reciprocated by our overseas customers and suppliers. This was excellent for our manufacturers because Britain could make more goods more cheaply and transport them speedily and at less cost than could any of our rivals. For farmers and landowners Free Trade seem to spell ruin for without tariffs imposed by the 'Corn Laws' to protect British grain our flour markets were flooded by imports sold at less than half the cost of home produce.

In Kendal Anti-Corn Law repealers won every seat on the Council and when

Above: *Reverse side of the Society's silver medal showing already out of date longhorns and pigs and poultry which were rarely shown and a non-Westmorland background.* Photos: Warwick Dickinson Photography

55

Richard Cobden   *John Bright*
The most hated statesmen amongst farmers in the 1840's
'The apostles of free trade'

the Corn Laws were abolished the prospect of cheap bread for the town workers was marked by celebratory rioting in the streets and the hoisting of a flag on the Town Hall. In his speech at the 1847 show Alderman Thompson tried to put on a brave face: 'The present time is no time for relaxation. We must buckle on the armour and fight the good fight now that the legislature has thought it proper to let in on them selves a whole host of foreign enemies.' But he and everyone else feared the worst. For once the landed interests as represented by the supporters of the Kendal Agricultural Society and Show were as out of favour as much as they feared they would be out of pocket.

Never in the next half century did the Society forget or forgive the 'betrayal' of British agriculture. As late as 1881 the President of the Show Frank Atkinson Argles of Eversley, Heversham, denounced Free Trade although his own wealth came as much from Free Trade commerce in Liverpool as it did from his wife's estates in the Lyth Valley: 'When we began Free Trade we had machinery which was superior to all other countries but foreigners had benefited from our intelligence and copied our machines and now produce them at a cheaper rate than we can.... We have cheap bread but what is the use of cheap bread if we have no wages and no employment to pay for it?' In 1887 Captain Bagot of Levens Hall told the luncheon guests that 'corn was imported from San Francisco to London at the same rate as it was carried from Kendal to London - 25s a ton'. Earlier the Kendal MP the Liberal Free Trader Alderman Whitwell had had difficulty in addressing the 1863 show dinner: 'The time was past when even the agricultural interest which was one of the largest and most powerful could obtain any preference of interest of the country at large though many including himself would look over it in the House'. Though, as in the 1930's and 1990's, there was more behind the farmers' constant moan that ruin was staring them all in the face the picture was not all black. Refrigerated meat imports were still decades away. While cereals plummeted the price of Westmorland beef rose from 4d a pound in 1849 to 8d a pound in 1866 when it dropped for a while before picking up and improving in later decades. Even when the first frozen lamb from New Zealand wafted in during the 1880's the demand for home produced meat was growing but then as the century ended the foreign threat was real. In 1895 Mr Paget Tomlinson told the Society that 10 million tons of dead meat had been imported in the half year ended June 30th. Happily, however, a relative decline in the growth of meat sales had been counterbalanced by the invention of metal milk kits and the organisation of 'milk trains' to cater for an unquenchable urban demand for the dairy products.

Urban industry had in fact always sustained and even stimulated the rural economy. A fortune made in the Welsh iron industry and other more local enterprises enabled the Kendal born Alderman Thompson to buy the Underley Estate at Kirkby Lonsdale which provided the agricultural base for his descendants the Earl and Countess of Bective and Lord and Lady Henry Bentinck to become the major patrons of the show up until the Second World War.

Fortunately, also, townsfolk did not live on bread alone. 'As long as the tall chimneys of Lancashire and Yorkshire smoke' extolled Crayston Webster of Beetham Hall in 1867 'so long will the Westmorland farmer have a never failing demand for his produce of mutton, cheese and wool'. Grain should, therefore, make way for more grass and, accordingly, W. E. Maude told the Kendal Farmers' Club in 1862 'we cannot on the generally thin soils of this county compete in quality and quantity with the grain grown in the United States...grazing...is...the proper course for Westmorland farming'. But as Crayston Webster also said, 'all kinds of reforms are slow to accomplishment, so hard is it to move out of the accustomed track'. Thus although between 1850 and 1900 the arable area of the county reduced by about a quarter there was no corresponding increase in permanent grass. Nevertheless the number of graziers and farmers in Westmorland stayed steady with 2719 in 1851 and 2589 in 1881 and there were still over 2000 in c.1900. Even so the percentage of agricultural workers declined from 26.5% in 1851 to 14% in 1911. Working in all weathers from dawn to dusk, with 'keeping in with 't' mester an't his missus' the only form of security for his pay and his 'tied' cottage, the farm servant's way of life was by most town standards frugal and feudal. 'The labour of a hand in Westmorland is hard, and the hours are long,' wrote Garnett in 1911, 'but the food is good and sufficient'. In fact their diet consisted principally of potatoes, tea sweetened abundantly with imported sugar with in good times a scragg of a joint weekly eked out by the odd rabbit and the less saleable portions of the back yard pig.

Hiring fairs still provided, literally, a labour market. To later generations, accustomed to job centres and c.v.'s, the idea of selling oneself in the street let alone the terminology of 'sound boy' or 'best woman' seems as odd as it sounds immoral. Yet twice a year Stricklandgate and the Market Place in Kendal were thronged with farm servants putting themselves out for hire, their availability being shown by the donning of a straw in their hats. Throughout the nineteenth century the custom was in full swing and, indeed, it did not die away completely until the 1950's. Compounding the Westmorland farmers' problems in the 1840's was the high cost of labour when many potential workers were lured to well paid navvying on the main line railway. In 1846 when the line was being built from Milnthorpe to Shap the wage of male farm servants doubled from £7 to £14 per half year, with 'keep and washing'. But the next year the rate dropped back to as low as £3 for six months. The highest recorded wage in the nineteenth century was £20 for 'good men' for the half year at the Kendal Hirings in 1872. Twenty years later 'best men' were only commanding £15 to £17. Apart from a prize of £1 being offered as long service award for farm servants in 1851 hardly any reference was made by the show authorities to their hired servants. At the 1857 show the Rev J. Simpson criticised Hirings saying 'it was highly desirable that we should have some knowledge of the master. Farm men ought to be guarded against farmers like Old Single bread who would not allow them to double their oat bread.'

The period was the heyday of the large, highly capitalised tenant farmers many of whom like William Handley of Greenhead and William Ellison of Sizergh were richer and more important than most local squires of fifty years earlier. To them grumbling and enterprise went together. 'Tha's touched t' reet spot there John' exclaimed one guest at the show's 1853 dinner when Mr Newby, one of the judges of crops, suggested that just as there were prizes for good tenants there should also be a prize for 'the most liberal landlord because there were many farms where the gates and buildings were in such a state that the tenant was out of pocket'. Even so it was the tenants rather than their landlords who called the tune in the Society's affairs.

The 1875 committee list reflects the dominance of bigger tenants and also of the geographical spread of members who lived right across South Westmorland but with only John Browne of Troutbeck coming from Lakeland and none from Eden or Shap. They were William Atkinson of Burneside Hall, Joseph Burrow, Bradley Field, James Bell, Overthwaite, John Browne, Troutbeck, A. Fulton, Sedgwick, James Gibson, Kendal, William Handley, Greenhead, John Harrison Jnr., Low Levens, John Holme, Owlett Ash, Milnthorpe, William Key, Casterton

William Handley's Greenbead Farm in decline c.1970 but still showing his enormous stock buildings and bull enclosures

Alderman Thompson's Cup, for best Stock of Store Cattle—£10 10s.

1 Mr. Obadiah Burrow, Heversham Hall
2 Mr. William Todd, Laverock Bridge
3 Mr. Rowland Parker, Moss End
4 Mr. Thomas Todd, The Green
5 Mr. John Scott, Greenhead
6 Mr. Richard Willison, Tullythwaite Hall
7 Mr. William Faulkner, Middleshaw

Mr. J. Benn's Cups, for the best Crop of Turnips sown with Guano alone —£7 7s.; 2nd £3 3s.

1 Mr. Joseph Watson, Madgegill
2 Mr. Thomas Powley, Beathwaite Green
3 Mr. Joseph Leece, (withdrawn)
4 Mr. Rowland Ewan, Three Mile House
5 Mr. William Todd, Laverock Bridge
6 Mr. Richard Willison, Tullythwaite Hall
7 Mr. Rowland Parker, Moss End
8 Mr. Thomas Strickland, Low Fair Bank
9 Mr. William Jopson, Brunt Knott
10 Mr. John Wilson, Over Staveley

Entries for 1850 show

Old Hall, Rowland Parker, Moss End, Preston Patrick, and F. Punchard the Underley agent, Kirkby Lonsdale. Regarding the Society the landlords' function was to turn up at the show with as impressive an equipage as possible, to donate and to present prizes. Throughout the period a full range of titled or at least 'esquired' local aristocrats served as show presidents and graced - generally verbosely - the dinner or luncheon. 1863 was a typical year when the 'Chair was taken by R. Musgrove Esq., supported on the right by the Earl of Suffolk, W. Marshall Esq., MP, W. Hassell Esq., Admiral Elliot, The Hon. Mr Petre, Lt. Col. Salmon, Thomas Scott Esq., Sir Stuart Donaldson, Henry Howard Esq., Captain Harrison, Captain Smith. The vice chair was taken by Timothy Featherstonehaugh of the College supported by C. Featherstonehaugh, J.W. Marshall, Thomas Parker, the Rev S. J. Butler and leading agriculturists'. Naturally on such occasions the importance of maintaining the rural status quo was stressed. Lord Derby told the luncheon in 1895 that 'the landlord and tenant system was good. Few of the men who emigrated to the USA or Canada thinking to be free from the landlord are in as good a position as they thought they would be when they started out'.

Judging by the press reports of all the shows from the 1840's to the end of the century, despite all the prophets of gloom in the dinner tent, there was so little wrong with local agriculture that no one could possibly have wished to leave Westmorland.

A fresh start rather than the beginning of the end for British agriculture was indeed indicated by the Society's activities in the 1840's. A new secretary Reg. Remington was appointed and although he only stayed in office for five years he implemented the new constitution adopted by the Society.

Under the new rules the show's district was enlarged to include the County of Westmorland and anywhere within 30 miles of Kendal. The latter provision proved to be significant as a large number of exhibitors, especially of horses, came from the Lancaster area and from Furness. Three judges who were not on the committee were to be appointed in future. This did not stop grumbles and in 1852 there were demands that more judges should be brought to expedite events on show day. Even then judges could hardly have been totally impartial as very few came from away and some were well known local farmers. In 1862, for instance, the farm inspectors were Christopher Gibson of Selside, R. Just of Natland, Edward Martindale of Benson Hall; the judges of cattle and of Leicester sheep were T. Oddy of Halifax and George Drewry of Holker and for horses, fell sheep and pigs John Irving of Shap Abbey and Thomas Kendal of Lawkland. Later judges from distant parts were brought in and the homes of judges for the 1895 show included Aberdeenshire, Morpeth, Lincolnshire, Kirkubrightshire, Lanarkshire, Carlisle, Shropshire, Oxfordshire and Brighton. The result was a falling off of complaints: 'It is now a curiosity' ran the 1897 report, 'to see a man in a hot temper awaiting an opportunity to go for the judges. Judges may be criticised but no one seems to doubt their honesty. A few years ago it was quite common to find farmers who firmly believed that a few half crowns judiciously spent would go a long way to gaining a prize'.

The 1840 Spring Cattle Show was the last to be held on Beast Banks. The Easter 'entire horse' shows continued in the town and from 1845, when thoroughbreds were included for the first time, were held generally on the New Road, until the 1900's. A more general horse show, where the exhibits were not even classified into agricultural, roadster or hunters, was also held in October until they were included in the main show. There were also ploughing competitions and the like which were popular enough and earned lengthy press coverage. Nevertheless from c.1840 the organisation of the main show held in late September or early October became the Society's dominant object and activity. These were now held on fields on the eastern edge of the town, a situation made even more favourable when the railway station was opened at Longpool in 1846. An enclosed field also meant that spectators could be charged sixpence a head for admission.

In 1840 the venue was Braithwaite Meadow near Stramongate bridge. As it

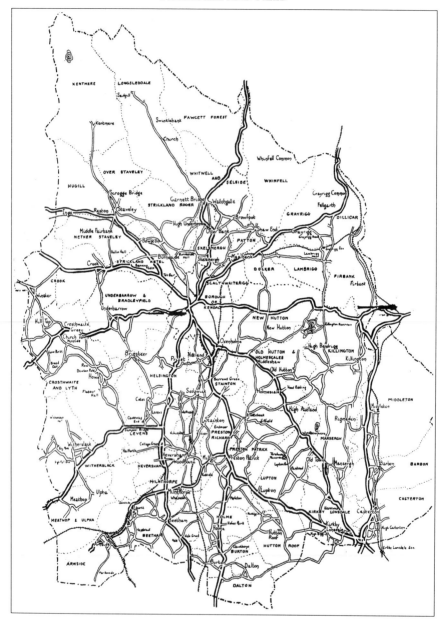

Though the show's 'district' included the whole county and beyond most entries came from south Westmorland

was a 'large and commodious field' there was ample room for the 135 entries in 24 classes. The show was still restricted to cattle but contrary to the trend for the next 70 years the largest entry was 21 for dairy cows for which the winner was Richard Willison. So successful did the new arrangements seem that at the dinner George Wilson of Dallam Tower, grandson of the founder Daniel, predicted that 'the winter of the society is past and the spring is at hand'. From 1841 to 1846 the show ground was at the top of Castle Street in Peat Lane. Here it expanded progressively. There were two silver cups and £100 in prizes in 1845 with 191 entries for 39 classes which grew the next year to 228 consisting of 41 farm entries, 87 for cattle, 50 sheep and wool, 8 pigs and 42 horses. Unfortunately, because of the depressed markets during the peak of the Anti-Corn Law troubles, members' subscriptions were mostly unpaid and the gate money of 6d per spectator did not cover the expenses and so all prize money was withheld! The Society was £122 in debt and perhaps its parlous state was a reason why in the same year - 1846 - a rival calling itself 'the Cumberland and Westmorland Agricultural Society' had been formed. With the support of Lord Lonsdale this body could not fail to do well but although there were migratory shows at Appleby in 1848 and 1852, Kirkby Stephen in 1862 and Shap in 1875 it mainly drew its support from Cumberland. Over the years the Kendal and Westmorland Society successively rejected offers of amalgamation with this and other societies. Even in bad years Kendal Show outshone other shows and remained 'The' show for most of South Westmorland but it did not shine alone. Burton-in-Kendal Agricultural Society founded in 1833 was Kendal's oldest and most consistent competitor especially after it amalgamated with the Milnthorpe Show (first held in 1836) in 1857 and later with the Carnforth Show. Over to the east the Lunesdale Show at Kirkby Lonsdale was formed in 1839 and the Appleby and Kirkby Stephen Show in 1841. To the north the Penrith Agricultural Society founded in 1836 drew support from Eden and East Cumberland. This became the Cumberland and Westmorland Agricultural Society in 1846 and although most of its shows were held outside the Kendal area it held a gigantic show at Milnthorpe in 1878 whose entries of 683 were only three less than for that year's Kendal Show. In 1880 even the Milnthorpe Show had nearly 600 entries, not far short of the number for Kendal. Other popular village shows included Crook Fair started in 1838, Brough 1848, Staveley 1851, Windermere 1853, Crosthwaite and Underbarrow 1859, Orton 1860, Shap 1861 and Dufton 1863. There were also specialist shows restricted to one species of which the most enduring was the Milburn Tup Show first held in 1853. Sheep were far more important in the northern shows like Milburn and Brough which may account for their relative insignificance at Kendal throughout most of the period.

Cattle were another matter and as Kendal Show was always held either in the third or fourth week in September its results set the seal on competitors who had been successful elsewhere. By the 1870's The *Westmorland Gazette* was chauvinistically championing 'our' show as the 'imprimatur' of all cattle shows including The Great Yorkshire and the Royal. Even so the reports of Shap Show generally printed in the same edition as that of the Kendal were often as lengthy and as glowing.

Kendal had two main reasons for its popularity. Being held on the edge of the county's largest town it could attract hoards of sixpenny spectators and above all the Show Field was near the railway station. Even stock from quite near at hand came by rail. Each year William Handley of Greenhead loaded his prize animals onto special cattle wagons at Hincaster junction from where they were conveyed the five miles into Kendal. Indeed William's national renown must have been partly due to the ease with which his nearness to the main line enabled him to transport his stock all round the country so that quite regularly it was reported that one of his Kendal prize winners had been successful hundreds of miles away a day or two previously.

Between 1847 and 1849 the show was 'held in the field between the canal and the river sometimes called the soldier's field'. For the '*annus mirabilis*' - 1847 - there was contradictory report that 'the show of stock was poor but as good as in former times'. The financial picture was, however, starkly clear. Premiums were down by £90 and the show's expenses of £30 were having to be met out of a reserve of £141. Entries and finances picked up in 1848 but the Society's difficulties grew when the Secretary John Pickthall, appointed only two years previously, resigned. His successor William Longmire proved to be the show's salvation. Immediately he organised a carcass competition but the prize money available for five classes for mutton, veal and beef only amounted to £2 10s. Not surprisingly in 1849 the *Gazette* reported 'it cannot be pronounced a first class show'. Gate takings at £14 represented only about 600 visitors and entries amounting to a mere 166 were down in all classes.

The next year an increase in rural confidence was reflected by a rise in entries to 199 which combined with a new secretary to produce a better show on a new ground. This was 'the large field in the occupation of Mr John Hulley on the north side of the Windermere Railway'. The new form of transport continued to be advertised. In 1854 it was reported that 'the annual exhibition of the society was held in the field usually appropriated for the purpose near the Railway Station'. Mr Longmire had 'affected great improvements' with 'two enclosures for cattle under award, by which the judges for cattle and for sheep and for horses and pigs were enabled to perform their duties simultaneously and the business of the day was greatly expedited...as was there being...only two judges and not three.' In case of dispute a judge from another class could be brought in but this had not been necessary. In 1851 entries rose to 358 and in 1852 although this number was not exceeded the reviewer pronounced the display at 'Longpool' the 'best show ever seen in Kendal'.

By the time William Longmire retired as Secretary in 1858 the show had not only strengthened its reputation in agricultural circles, it had also become a highlight in the social calendar. In 1859 there was 'a large attendance on the ground including many of the fair sex and among the visitors we observed the Earl and Countess of Bective and Miss Darby (*sic*)'. Rearrangements made by the new secretary Joseph Swainson were reported in 1861 when there was 'a quite separate' ring for sheep. A further 'novel feature was presented by the booths being entirely taken (at a fee of £6 10s) by the tee-total interest who vended tea, coffee, and other anti-alcoholic refreshments but they did not seem very extensively patronised and the consequence was that the lanes adjacent to the show drove an extraordinary trade'. In other words the pubs close to the ground like The Duke of Cumberland, The Castle, the Prince of Wales' Feathers and the Farmers Arms all within a few hundred yards were packed out and uproarious. A major deterrent to attendance by the rougher element occurred in 1863 when the show transferred from Saturday to Wednesday apparently because this day was more convenient for the railways. But the advantage of the day 'was not proven the weather being unfavourable' and attendance was down. Moreover entries in cattle were down from 83 in 1862 to 72 and in horses from 119 to 103. There was, however, a steep rise in sheep from 64 to 345 and with good augurs for the future an innovation of 'horse leaping for hunters' drew a large and interested crowd. Attendance remained good in the 1860's even in

The new name on the Society's medal

1865 when 'in spite of terror of contagion from much talked of pestilence' entries were up. The plague was a grim reality next year and although judging went ahead on farms for the Grayrigg Show such an arrangement was impossible for the far flung Kendal entrants and so the show was abandoned. A special licence had to be obtained from the Lords in Council for the 1868 show to go ahead when at this stage, perhaps to redeem its pre-eminence, 'the Kendal' was renamed 'the Westmorland and Kendal District Agricultural Society's Exhibition'. 1868 also saw the retirement after eleven years of William Longmire who was presented with 'a handsome gift of plate'. The 1869 Wednesday show reportedly attracted the 'largest attendance ever' but sadly, again because of Foot and Mouth Disease, there was no show in 1870.

Only stringent measures enabled the 1871 show to go ahead: 'Mr Superintendent Bird and the Veterinary Surgeon Mr W. Simpson examined every beast to come onto the ground'. Inevitably cattle were reduced in number but the overall entries were up by 120 on 1869. To the credit of Mr Swainson arrangements were said to be 'excellent' and his general planning of the field was kept for many years. 'On either of the entrance gates were trade stalls displaying feed stuffs and impliments'. In the foreground on the main field were the cattle stalls, from beyond which 'stretched a spacious hippodrome from the end of the grandstand to near the end of the field with two stands on either side'. The horse ring was in the north west corner along with the pens for stationing horses. Rather unsavourily the luncheon tent was placed between the sheep pens and the hippodrome to the east beyond which a further refreshment tent for the hoi polloi 'spread its ample dimensions while on the extreme a field had been annexed for the display of agricultural horses'.

Show day started early with judging commencing at 9.15am. This took all morning and the first prizes were distributed in the butter tent at 1.30pm. Horse leaping followed at 2pm and the day concluded, except for the clearing up by the ground staff, with dinner at 3.30pm at the Commercial Hotel which was formerly the Station and later the County Hotel. The only criticism in 1871 was that better fences were required for the horses. Worry and optimism born out of blissful ignorance of science were expressed by one of the after dinner speakers: 'I fear Foot and Mouth Disease but hope that if it comes it will be in a mild form and will leave the cattle better than they were before'.

A long lasting change occurred in 1874 when show day was fixed at the third Thursday in September. Unfortunately continued fears of Foot and Mouth meant that attendance was up and down for the next few years. Even so in the 'bad' year 1878 a sunny day helped draw a crowd of over 4,000 and complaints that the cattle ring was too small. Rain at the 1879 show 'severely tested the resources upon which the Westmorland and Kendal and District Society depends for the maintenance of its highly useful operation'. 'Incessant rain all day' again spoilt the show in 1881 but a new entrance 'through the barn enabled money and check takers to carry out their duties without incon-venience...while...on the cricket field the pavilion served as a grandstand and chairman's and Secretary's room' but, the reviewer moaned, there was nowhere for the reporters while out in the field there was 'no cover for the band, not even boards to stand on'.

A musical background to the show had first been provided by the Juvenile Catholic Band in 1852 and the Workhouse Drum and Fife Band had played in 1860. From 1867 onwards the regular band was that of the Third Westmorland Volunteers who gallantly played whatever the weather even though, as in 1881, 'they were frequently overcome by the ruder voices of the North West gale'. But in 1884 they were not asked to play 'and the absence of music was greatly felt. It will be for the committee to decide if they can abolish so popular and attractive an accessory to the exhibition.' Sadly such pleas fell on deaf ears and for the next twenty years the chatter of the crowd and the neighing, mooing, baaing and

BREAD, BEEF AND BUTTER 1840 - 1898

snorting of the stock, all competing with the clank and sizzle of the locomotives in the adjoining marshalling yards, went unmuted.

A happier development occurred in 1884 when on the retirement of Mr Swainson Messrs George and Edwin Hoggarth, who were professional land agents, were appointed secretaries. Eventually Major G.L. Hoggarth became the sole secretary and held the office until the First World War. Happily too the Hoggarths' first show was particularly successful with the best ever attendance though regrettably, despite the recent lifting of restrictions on the movement of stock, entries in the cattle classes were still lower than before the Foot and Mouth scare.

In 1891 the first comparative tables were published. These showed that entries were up to 634 from 600 in the previous year and that sheep entry had increased from 200 to 229 but cattle had dropped from 105 to 94. From then on there was an overall increase in entries with 811 entries in 1894, 931 in 1896, 975 in 1897 and 878 in 1898.

There was also a corresponding alleviation of the Society's main worry - finance. The problem was always the same: when times were hardest for the farmers the Society needed their support more though they were least able to provide it; not that they were over keen to put their hands inside their pockets. Way back in 1848 Mr Ellison regretted to see 'two of the biggest farmers voting to keep premiums at 5s'. He then proposed that premiums should be increased in proportion to the acreage farmed with for instance under 100 acres staying at 5s, 200 10s, 300 15s, 400 £1 but this too was rejected. The old 5s sub which included free entry to the show ground persisted. Fortunately membership grew but this improvement led to further grumbles from Mr Ellison. Years ago the society's expenses were £45 and Mr Wilson used to give ten golden sovereigns in a bag. Now upwards of £150 came from subscriptions and the labour of collecting it was very great. Even so for well over the next hundred years collectors went round their neighbours for the annual 'subs' rather than insisting on payment by postal or bankers order. Gate money was a relatively minor source of income in the mid century with receipts varying from £57 in 1862, £45 in 1863 but from the 're-birth' of the show in the 1870's takings rose to £175 4s 6d in 1874, £209 in 1890 and £238 in 1896. Prize money also increased from £89 in 1850, £118 in 1851 - when second prizes were offered for the first time in every class - to around £300 throughout the 1870's and 1880's after which they rose in the 1890's to over £500 in 1898.

The Society's strength on the eve of its centenary demonstrated its success in sticking to its principal aims of promoting agriculture while also diversifying the show's attractions.

Improvements in cultivation and general husbandry as revealed in knowledge of agriculture and in the overall maintenance of a farm and of all types of stock remained the Society's main objectives. During the 1870's the Society organised an essay prize sponsored by the Earl of Bective and other landowners. The topics chosen probably reflect the balance of the Society's interest at the time: 'Farm management' 1874 and 1875 for which there were ten entrants, 'Improvement of Waste land' 1876: 3 entrants, 'The profitable Management of Grass' 1877: 7 entrants and 'The Breeding and Rearing of cattle' 1878: 8 entrants. The winners were Richard Taylor of Newhouse in 1875, J.C. Boustead of Hackthorpe in 1875, William Cottam of Foulshaw and as second A.B. Taylor of Newhouse in 1876, John Garnett of Wyresdale and as second in 1877 John Noble of Helsington. In 1878 John Noble and A.B. Taylor were again successful as first and second prize winners respectively. In 1875 the entrants adopted nom de plumes: W. Cottam called himself 'Agricola', A.B. Taylor, 'Practice of Science', J. Armistead of Firbank, 'One who delights with progress' and J. Gormall of Wyresdale, 'Q.E.D.' Within their main brief they also had to address three main topics: 1) the planting of shelter, 2) rabbits, 3) adulterous substances especially bone dust. Unfortunately only the efforts and solutions contained in the prize winning essays (which were published) have come to light. Most of the essayists paid greatest attention to crops supported by such hoary clichés as 'it is better to farm a small farm well than to take a holding that is too big for the available capital' and 'a good head is worth two pairs of hands'.

The crop inspectors' report was always solemnly read at the show dinner and the Society laid down complex rules for their guidance. Thus in 1895 'it was resolved that instructions be given to the Inspectors when inspecting Crops to inspect the 12 rows and measure the 100th part of an acre at various widths of the stitches varying from 88" to 35" taking the requisite length of each stitch & work them out by a table which Mr J G Webster has promised to provide'.

Considerable attention was paid to roots and to the means of fertilising them. Prizes offered by guano and bone meal merchants whose products at first were imported during the 1830's by the Whittaker family through the port of Milnthorpe became widely available with the development of the railways in the1850's. In 1850 prize winners for the best crop of turnips were spread across the district and included Robert Kendall, Sellet Hall, Thomas Powley, Beethwaite Green, Joseph Watson, Madger Gill, Rowland Parker, Moss End, Thomas Hayhurst, Millbridge, William Simm, Watercrook, John Scott, Greenhead, William Todd, Laverock bridge and Robert Willison, Tullythwaite Hall. The best farm for 'white and green crops' was Rowland Parker's at Moss End.

At almost all shows the presentation of the 'crops premiums' provided an opportunity for guests, judges and prize winners to ruminate on cultivation. In 1851 Mr Ellison boasted of how he had spread £100 of guano at 2 cwts an acre on his land and of how, as a result, he had obtained £150 worth of potatoes from seven and a half acres. Attempts to encourage small farmers to compete invariably fell on stony ground. In 1858 although there were 'increased entries for farm management' there was but one entry for farms not exceeding 50 acres 'which went to Mr Hudson'. The prize for the over 50 acre farm went to Mr T. Hawkrigg of Low Wray on the very edge of 'the Kendal district'. Mr Hawkrigg's turnips were especially commended 'as being very heavy but in want of a little more labour'. Periodically suggestions were made by the crop experts about how a small farm could be made, in effect, larger. In 1855 'Mr Fawcett in returning thanks to the judges expounded on the value of drainage which was still wanted round Kendal'. In a similar vein a judge told how a north Westmorland farmer had added two acres to one field (in reversing the trend of the previous 100 years), by grubbing out unnecessary hedges.

Fertilisers, whether new or old, remained the main issue. Some farmers used salt on root crops and in 1861 - no doubt towards the end of the post prandial refreshments - Mr Wakefield, the Society's treasurer, drew loud laughter when he had just 'peppered his turnips with salt but they were not as good as when he grew them without salt'. Valuable prizes were offered by merchants and by landlords for cultivation. From c. 1870 the Earl of Bective offered a ten guinea cup for the best grass of which the winner in 1871 (and in many subsequent years) was Rowland Parker of Moss End with William Atkinson of Burneside Hall as second. A silver tea and coffee service was the glittering prize presented by Messrs Morrison's manures to James Proctor of Low Blease, Old Hutton for the best three acre field of swede turnips in 1877.

The possibility of agricultural improvements was always stressed at the show in the after dinner speeches and, also, from the 1850's onwards by the displays on the 'Implements Stands'. 'It would be a great advantage' pronounced the Hon. Colonel Lowther MP, the chairman, in 1857 'if a small stream of steam engines were kept to go round and perform various operations on the farm when wanted...threshers would be especially useful'. That the technology was available was shown when, at the 1865 show, there were 'two machines for threshing and dressing corn by Messrs Williamson of this town. They were worked by a small locomotive and we understand are most effective implements'. Even more spectacular was a demonstration of 'Abyssinian Well boring' in 1869 when, on the field 'a well boring operation was carried out to a depth of 24 feet and the amount of water was copious'. The device made by Williamsons from 'North's patent' was formed from 'pipes like gas pipes culminating in a bulbous spike'. Literally moving with the times were the displays by Mr Gooding, who in 1869 exhibited several 'handsome carriages and coaches and an omnibus destined for the King's Arms'. 'Six horse steam engines' appeared in 1878 along with displays by Mr Huck the saddler and of the 'Alpha gas making apparatus which was put to a severe test by violent gusts of wind'. During a depressed year 1879 implements were sparse except for the butter churns shown by E.W.

Thompson along with sewing and other domestic machines. But as an instance of the shape of things to come Messrs Whiteside and Co of Liverpool showed patent galvanised steel fencing.

The district had a surprisingly large number of agricultural engineers and in 1881 ploughs were shown by Staintons of Milnthorpe, Williamsons and, for the first time, by Gilbert Gilkes and Gordon of Kendal, Parker of Natland and Messrs Huck and son of Endmoor. Presaging the twentieth century's farmyard architectural catastrophe Mr W. Middleton showed in 1886 'some useful articles made from corrugated iron including a stack cover and a Dutch barn'.

Depending on the state of trade the extent of the displays varied from year to year. Only Messrs Croft and Richardson showed implements including a full range of bicycles in 1892; otherwise there was just cattle feed, seeds and potions on display. It was in 1892 that Dog Biscuits were mentioned for the first time. They were shown by a local maker Mr Hind who for over twenty years had 'exhibited his sheep salves and dog medicines'. Amidst all the 'paraphernalia by the Bibby Cake Company and others' T. Moffat of Oxenholme showed in 1894 'specimens of fattening meal, moss litter by the Lound Coal Company'. There were also displays of kitchen ranges by Messrs Whittle and Son of Whitehaven and as for the previous fifteen years of Singer sewing machines. As part of the Singer's sales gimmick the *Gazette* report of the 1896 show stated that their 'sewing machines have lately had a boom in connection with a visit of Li Hung Chang who took with him as a present from the manufacturers elegant specimens for the Empress of China'. Nevertheless, all press reports stressed the display of agricultural equipment, rather than household gadgets or other attractions, as being a major feature of the show. Thus after praising Mr Croft's 'strawsonizer' the reporter sneered 'it would be better to encourage the show of implements rather than spending money on useless dog prizes'.

Dog classes for rough and smooth coated dogs and bitches first appeared in c. 1887 but it was not until the twentieth century that they were taken seriously. 'It is now over twenty five years', ran the 1890 report, 'that dogs were first shown in Cumberland but we do not see the value of such a class at a show like Kendal's. The fact is that the modern fancy collie dog is of no practical value whatever to Westmorland farmers'. Furthermore, the reporter whined, 'there were only two or three weedy looking dogs at the benches with coats out of condition'. Nonetheless there were 17 dogs listed among the prize winners! E. Birkett's 'Butcher's Boy' was praised in 1893 but once again there were 'no dogs fit for the fells'. Mr Birkett was indeed the first local champion dog breeder. His rough coated 'Burneside Perfection' won the bitches class for 'a dog belonging to a tenant or butcher'. In 1896 he was, however, beaten into second place by Mr W. Clark's dog while Messrs Walling and Dean's 'Lancaster Countess ' won the rough coated bitches section. For once the report was quite complimentary. 'A

Not like the modern Border collie - a fell working sheepdog c.1890

most pleasing feature was the working dogs belonging to tenants, the winner being Mr T. Tomlinson of New Hutton with a clean little animal, full of vigour and instinct and well qualified as a farmer's help.' An equally good specimen was a sable and white dog of Mr Kendal of Kilne Hall called 'Farleton Bright'. For the ninety-ninth show in 1898 Mr Birkett regained his laurels when he won with 'Forget me not' a bitch by 'Cherot' out of 'Sefton Hero'.

Dog classes were one of several minor and inconsistent sections which came and went at the show. Pigs featured in the premiums section in the 1840's and there were eight entries in 1846 and 13 in 1850 for the class for 'best boar/sow of large or small breed'. In 1855 there were only three competitors: William Ellison, Joseph Burrow of Crosthwaite and William Bownass of Bowness. 1859 was a good year with 19 entries and the main prize was won by W.E. Maude esq. Entries dropped to only four in 1879; 1881 was described as 'a good average year' but even then there were only ten entries. Thereafter the section was dropped and was not revived for many years.

Poultry was considered to be quite important at least in the general farm stock category in the early years. Sections were introduced at the 1848 show for geese, turkeys, ducks and barndoor fowls but entries were never heavy. After 1853 when the first separate poultry show was held in Kendal 'nearly all the entries were from and the prizes taken by Westmorland fanciers, or those living just over the border.' As a result interest in entering classes at the show fell off and the section was abandoned. From the 1890's eggs were included in the 'butter' classes but attracted little support.

Cheese also appeared on the schedule from time to time although Westmorland, unlike neighbouring North Lancashire and Craven, was never a great cheese making county. During the 1870's John Wakefield esq. gave a premium for the best hundredweight of cheese and in 1877 there were five entries when Thomas Thompson of Lambrigg won the first prize and George Edmonson of Beetham won the second. Entries dwindled from then on and disappeared around 1881. In 1887, however, 'a large basket of cream cheese was displayed in the butter tent by Mrs Strickland of Crook' but this was not part of a competition.

From the 1860's butter classes became increasingly competitive and controversial. Before that time there were few entries except in 1855 when there were 18 competitors for prizes offered by Messrs Dixon. Although all the butter would have been made by the farmers' wives, daughters and dairy maids prizes went to the - male - farmers who, in 1855, included Mr Matthews of Selside Hall, James Reed, Henry Fawcett of Sedbergh with William Scott and Jos. Watson highly commended.

The situation was transformed in 1869 when Lady Alice Kenlis (later the Countess of Bective) inaugurated a new butter competition for a piece of plate which attracted 67 entries. 'The judges' it was pointed out 'have a very difficult task in obtaining the faculty of discriminating between 67 samples of butter all of it no doubt good and implying a nicety of gustative powers that seems

'almost miraculous'. In fact, 'gustatively', it was even more of an ordeal as each sample consisted of six pounds of butter split into half pound packs each of which apparently had to be tasted! The competition was never quite as popular again but in 1871 there were 47 entries for butter made without salt. Mr James Thompson of Castle Meadows took the plate and the second prize winner who got 10s was Mr C. Wilson of High Park and the third (5s) was Mr Henry Dobson of Park House. James

A silver kettle presented by Countess Bective to Mrs P. Cummings of Howgill for 'Best Butter' 1878

72

Thompson won several times again but in 1878, when there were 50 competitors, the 'first honours went to Mr P. Cummings for a rich basket. The Countess of Bective presented her prizes personally 'accompanying each with a few kindly words'. So good was the butter on show in 1879 according to one speaker that 'its quality ought to silence the charges made against Westmorland butter'. But the butter critics persisted. In 1880 Mr Lowther said that farmers' wives and daughters should concentrate on the arts of the dairy - 'they should work the churn not play the piano'. 'The competition seems to grow in interest year by year' was the verdict in 1881 although at 37 the entries were nearly half those of earlier years. For the first time the successful dairy maids - or rather matrons - were named as Mrs Thornburrow of Toadpool and Mrs Atkinson of Low Groves. In order to promote better butter techniques the Countess substituted Cunningham Patent Butter Workers for her prize in 1885 but after a year or so the message got through that the farmers' wives preferred a nice piece of plate for the parlour rather than an implement for the dairy as their reward. In 1893 the main prizes were a silver tea pot and a crystal and silver mounted biscuit jar.

New methods were being adopted, however, and in 1888 both first prize winners Mrs Dargue of Burneside Hall and Mrs Atkinson of Overthwaite revealed that they had both used 'butter makers'. This technique meant that salt need not be used and the improved flavour enabled them to charge 2d a pound more for their product.

It was at the 1886 show that Lady Olivier Taylour - later Lady Henry Bentinck - first assisted her mother in presenting the butter prizes. When Mrs Rowlandson went to collect her prize both titled ladies 'engaged her in conversation for two or three minutes' [wow!].

The male speech makers, who had almost certainly never made butter with or without modern gadgets, were always adept in offering advice. Mr Wakefield, in 1885, gave an elementary and probably novel lesson in basic hygiene: 'The great object in butter making was to keep the hand from the butter as contact with the hand could contain a certain amount of impurity which could lead to putrefaction'. Similarly Mr C.W. Wilson, the squire of Rigmaden, urged the use of a milk separator which could enable you to 'get 1s 5d a pound'. He went on to say 'that it is often said that the butter basket paid the rent and this made it an important question for those who received the rent!' No doubt the Underley agent Mr Punchard thought the same when he urged butter makers to use the methods as taught by the newly opened Cumberland and Westmorland agricultural school at Newton Rigg.

That improvements were urgently required had been demonstrated in 1890 when Lord Brougham and Vaux uttered one of the most notorious statements ever made about Westmorland agriculture when he declared 'that he had been sold butter at 6d a pound which was an absurd price as it was fit only to grease wheels'.

For a time the modern methods seemed to be successful and in 1897 all the prize winners had used the County Schools techniques. But this was not enough to suit the Countess of Bective who in possibly the most dramatic gesture in the history of the show upstaged Lord Brougham and Vaux's attack by withdrawing her butter prizes. The Countess did not, of course, wish on this occasion to indulge in even a few minutes of conversation with the butter ladies but left it to her neighbour Mr Paget Tomlinson to read out her sensational justification for her apparently ungracious act. Her Ladyship wrote 'the prizes have entirely failed to effect the results for which they were intended when they were first offered almost thirty years ago; if all the butter was as good as was on show there would be no problems but most of it will not keep for 50 out of 52 weeks. As further proof I have personally tested the butter sold on Kendal market and am satisfied that it is badly made, that it will not keep and that it is uneatable'. With 'candid friends' like this Westmorland agriculturists did not need enemies. Fortunately, however, their other - more successful - activities were well demonstrated at the show.

The main classes were always for cattle, sheep and horses. For exactly one hundred years from 1840 when Longhorns were exhibited at the last Beasts Banks Show until the Second World War, with the exception of two years in the 1920's, the cattle classes were exclusively for Shorthorns and the accounts of their entries and prize winners invariably made up half of the report of each show. In 1887 for instance the *Westmorland Gazette* after observing that 'the neighbourhood of Kendal is much more noted for the breeding of Shorthorns than it is for horses or sheep' devoted sixteen column inches to cattle and only two and a half to 'Sheep, Pigs and Dogs'. As early as 1846 there were 87 entries for cattle as against 50 for sheep, 42 for horses, 41 for farms and 8 for pigs. Even in the 'bad year' 1847 there were eight classes for cattle and 'keen competition' for the best yearling bull (won by Thomas Morton) and for Alderman Thompson's ten guinea premium for the best stock of store cattle. The Thompson Cup (later called after his son-in-law the Earl of Bective's cup) was for some twenty years the show's principal award. In 1849 and 1850 the winner was John Scott of Greenhead whom Alderman Thompson hoped would 'long live to enjoy many a good glass of wine from it'. His hopes were more than fulfilled and John lived on to become a leading prize winner including that of 'best bull' in 1857. Moreover, John Scott by developing the pastures, buildings and stock at Greenhead paved the way for the farm's becoming one of the most renowned stock farms in the kingdom, especially for beef, during the long tenure of his successor William Handley.

In the late 1840'and 1850's some importance was given to dairy cattle and the 1850 report pronounced the 'heifers both two year olds and yearlings to be capital'. The stock of breeding cows was, however, poor except for the best fat cow won by William Ellison junior, and the best stock of store cattle won by Thomas Todd of the Green, Lambrigg. 1850 also saw one of the first lady prize winners when Mrs Mary Fawcett of Skelsmergh Hall was judged to have the best managed farm.

In 1855 the *Westmorland Gazette* provided a detailed report of the winning farms which showed how important were cattle when compared to other forms of husbandry. The winner of the 'best managed farm' was Mr James Gibson who had two upland holdings. His farm at Cooper House, Selside, consisted of old meadow land 25 acres, fell land 20 acres, old 'carros' moor 24 acres, old inclosed land, mostly arable 139 acres amounting to 280 acres. His second holding at Long Well Farm comprised old meadow land 7 acres, fell allotment 15 acres and old inclosed land mostly arable 81 acres totalling 311 acres. The second prize winner was William Todd of Laverock Bridge who farmed old meadow land 24 acres, pasture 36 acres, arable 15 acres, (fell) allotment 15 acres amounting to 90 acres. That a very small farmer like William Todd was deemed to be worthy

A concentration on beef - part of the catalogue of
Westmorland and Kendal District Ag. Soc. fat stock show

13 Mr. T. J. Harrison, Singleton Park (roan), bred by Mr. J. Taylor, (no address given) fed by exhibitor.
14 Mr. T. Nelson, butcher, Stainton (roan), fed by Mr. Keightley, Old Hall
15 Mr. John Dixon, Carus Green (roan), bred by Mr. Mounsey, Penrith, fed by exhibitor (on sale).
16 Mr. Joseph Lewthwaite, Kendal (red), bred and fed by Mr. John Morton, Skelsmergh Hall.
17 Mr. Edward Rigg, Kendal (red and white), bred by Mr. Mattinson, Ravenstonedale, fed by Mr. J. Jordan, Kendal.
18 Mrs. Mary Wilson, Kendal (white), fed by Mr. J, Gibson, Cooper House.
19 Mr. Moses Hully, jun., Kendal (dark roan), bred and fed by Mr. John Mackereth, Barrows Green.
20 Mr. Moses Hully, sen., Kendal (red and white), bred and fed by Mr. John Strickland, Milton Moor.
fr-C · 21 Mr. Moses Hully, sen., Kendal (roan), bred by Mr. Richard Wilson, Hugil, fed by exhibitor.
22 Mr. Moses Hully, sen., Kendal (red and white), bred by Mr. T. W. Simm, Watercrook, fed by exhibitor.

1st awarded to No 2*2*-2nd to No *14*

CLASS 4—For the best FAT GALLOWAY or HIGHLANDER of any age £1.—Second best, 10s

23 Mr. George Robinson, butcher, Kendal (black), bred and fed by Hon. Gen. Upton, Lord's Plain Farm.
24 Hon. Gen. Upton, Lord's Plain Farm (black), bred and fed by exhibitor.
25 Mr. Jacob Joyce, Kendal (black), fed by Mr. Cropper, Eller Green.
26 Mr. Jacob Joyce, Kendal (black), fed by Mr. Cropper, Eller Green.

1st awarded to No 2*4*-2nd to No 2*3*.

of a prize shows that the durability and enterprise of the old Statesmen of Westmorland had persisted despite changes in tenure and husbandry. Nevertheless it was a great tenant William Ellison of Sizergh who won the premium for 'the best general stock'. His 330 acre farm held 25 milch cows, 71 other cattle all of his own breeding, 26 horses, 400 Leicester and Southdown sheep, 37 pigs, 35 turkeys, 52 geese, and 150 'barn door fowl all very good'. James Gibson of Cooper House was again successful being the second prize winner for 'a very useful stock' consisting of 43 cows in calf or milk, 10 two year old heifers, 4 yearling bullocks, 26 calves, one aged bull, 4 work horses, and other horses to the number of 13, two breeding sows and 20 young pigs, 40 half bred ewes and 80 fat sheep all being 'a very good stock in the hands of a tenant farmer'.

The outstanding farmer in the middle years of the century was William Ellison. As a joke at the 1850 show someone proposed his name in the toast to 'the unsuccessful exhibitors'. In retaliation William, retrieving his lamp from under any bushell, replied 'although he had only secured a second prize in one section he considered himself in reality to be very successful because more animals from his stallions and bulls, heifers and sheep had gained prizes than anyone else by a considerable number. He had the pleasure of receiving 396 prizes from the Kendal Agricultural Society. Of these 395 had been first prizes and although he had only gained a second prize for his bull...it was highly gratifying to see how many from his stock had got prizes. The fact was that his bull was so situated in his pasture that he had to look out upon the cows and as he could not get at them he fretted himself to death. They might laugh (they did in fact do so) but if any one of them was courting they would find it no laughing matter'. Semi-seriously he made a final excuse that 'his turnips had not won because his land was livery and so the turnips were not ready in time unlike when the show was held on the third Saturday in October (and not three weeks earlier) when he had won 15 times out of 23 years'.

Despite his enormous success Mr Ellison did not have a completely clear run and leading breeders amongst his contemporaries included A.W. Long of Low Bridge House for dairy, John Todd, Tenter End, breeding stock and J. Todd, Scaltherwaiterigg, W.E. Meade, Holmescales, William Bowness (or Bownass - the name is spelt in both forms in reports!) of Middleton Hall for general stock and heifers.

Bulls, however, had the most involved classification, took the best prizes, made the biggest news and sometimes elicited the most controversy. Thus in 1865 W.H. Wakefield 'Esq.' of Sedgwick House (though his beast was reared at Wellheads) came top out of 12 entries for 'best bull two years old and not exceeding six which had been in the possession of the exhibitor three months previous to the Show engaged to serve cows within the limits of Society during the succeeding nine months'. When Mr William Boulton of Park House, Ulverston, won the aged bull class in 1863 the animal was reported as being 'splendid...having enormous bulk and symmetry but some thought too fat for the purpose'. Nevertheless the Boulton beast or beasts went on to win at Kendal for the next three years until his bull which had also won at Lancaster a day or two previously 'got the green ribbon' at Kendal. A big row resulted at the dinner after Mr John Machell asked whether it was true that it had not got any stock for several years. In replying Mr F.C. Ellison said 'he had no information but the £5 prize money (about £250 in the values of 130 years later) would be withheld until August next year and in the meantime the matter would be dealt with'. Sadly no clear announcement seems to have been made as to whether Mr Boulton's probity or his bull's prowess were vindicated. 'All t' bother' seems to have put off more than Mr Boulton and his bull for in the following year, although there were 5 entries, only two bulls were shown respectively belonging to J. Morton of Skelsmergh Hall - who won - and Rowland Parker of Moss End. For the next year or two entries hardly improved until in 1869 the winners for Best Bull not exceeding six years were James C. Bowstead, Hackforth Hall, Penrith, W. Rowland Parker, Moss End and, for the first, William Handley, Greenhead. William also gained the second prize for the best yearling bull after John Wright of Greenhill, Penrith. The best heifer prizes went to Anthony Metcalf-Gibson, Ravenstonedale and R.W. Ashburner of Broughton-in-Furness who were regular winners in this class.

As William Handley began to sweep the bull prize board descriptions of the stock became fuller and more candid. Thus after a tussle in 1874, which took the judges over an hour to resolve, Mr Handley's yearling bull 'The Earl of Devon' was hailed as 'a roan with splendid loins, great depth and width of chest but with too narrow a chine and plain and deficient hindquarters'; Mr Ralph's 'Gondolier' was 'a bull of great width but insufficient loin' while Mr H. Parker's 'O Pure Gold' was 'a thick sappy white, possibly too short and wanting in loin but with splendid thighs'. The yearling bulls were won by 'the Earl of Clare', 'a small red and white bull with straight top, Flattish fore rib and coarse horn'.

In the same year William Handley won the Earl of Bective's ten guinea cup 'for the best store of cattle, half to be of the tenant's own breeding'. His stock also included the champion aged bull 'Sober Robin' whose 'barrel was too round but his symmetry too perfect to make his defeat an easy matter'. Finally to crown a triumphant show Mr Handley won the three cow section in which one of the rival cows was called curiously 'Prince Rupert'. In 1877 'Mr Handley swept most before him but he did not win in heifers or milk except for a three year old heifer but he did have two champion bulls and collected the time piece donated by Messrs Rhodes of Kendal for the best three shorthorns of any age'. By 1878 it was openly being stated that Mr Handley's success was putting off other

William Handley's shorthorn bull 'Pearl King' champion 'Aged Bull' 1888

competitors and there were allegations that his champion bull 'Royal Irwin' could not meet the rule to produce six living calves in the next six months. Nevertheless for best female he was beaten by Richard Taylor's 'Bracelet Third'. It was therefore a sensation in 1879 when 'Master Harbinger' belonging to 'Mr Handley who has proved over and over again that he can get to the top of this and any other show' and which had won at The Royal the previous week was beaten at Kendal by R. Taylor's 'Prince Louis'. Next year at what was now called 'one of the oldest cattle shows in the kingdom' 'Master Harbinger' won at Kendal as he 'was looking in much better condition than last year even though he has travelled hundreds of miles'. He won again in 1881 when the *Gazette* cheaply remarked he had a 'clean sweep as the restrictions on movement of cattle in Lancashire deprived the show of noted breeders like the Ashburners and Robinsons'. In 1882 'Master Harbinger' had been replaced as Greenhead's champion by 'Hesperous - a massive thick bull bred by Mr Aylmer his hindquarters and thighs were good but we did not quite like his bone'. Even so he easily beat Mr Wakefield's 'Baron Sedgwick'. In 1883 fear of disease which also led to a ban on entries from Cumberland deterred William Handley from showing his best beasts and the champion bull belonged to J.&J. Backs of Low Foot. Nevertheless he took most of the cups for best aged bulls in the next few years. His 1884 second winner 'Hiawatha' was 'a good specimen but wanted constant movement to keep out of sight a noticeable slackness on the back' but his champion 'Royal Ingram' had 'all points perfect though it looked like any ordinary animal'. 'Royal Ingram' also won again in 1885 'as a matter of course' but there was disappointment that Mr Handley's 'Royal Hovingham' could not be entered as 'it had been sold abroad for a gigantic sum'.

Repeatedly, William Handley's near monopoly of the most prestigious prizes was blamed for a decline in entries. When in 1888 Mr. Handley's 'Pearl King' won it was asked 'why have an aged bull class at all as Mr Handley supplied the only two entrants: very few people are prepared to 'make up' an animal they are using especially a valuable animal and it is very unwise to tempt people to make such a risky experiment.' In yearling bulls there were seven entries but only two turned up and the winner was, inevitably, Mr Handley's 'Lord Roseberry'. Mr Handley's rivals might well have thought that it was particularly appropriate that the name of his winning aged bull was 'Self Conceit'. A year or two later there were signs that William Handley dominance was waning. 'Royal Warrior' belonging to T.W. Hewetson of Calthwaite beat Mr Handley's great prize 'Macbeth' and he failed to take any prize in the class for the 'best pair of Shorthorns of any age'. In 1891 though many preferred Mr Handley's bull calf and 'there was many a Scotch bet with 2d stakes amongst friends as to the probable winner' he was unsuccessful. 'It seems' the *Gazette* speculated, 'that the skimmed milk for calves at New House, Overthwaite and Skelsmergh Hall...must be of superior quality to that of Greenhead'. It was, however, William's own fault that his aged bull 'Baron Ingram'(who at five years and nine months was the 'most aged' in the class) was beaten by 'a massive even, well grown animal belonging to W. and J.T. Taylor because he had sent better beasts, to other shows'. Even so he was also beaten in yearling bulls by Mr A. Cleasby of Pedge Croft, Sedbergh and in milk cows by Mr Thompson of The Lound. In 1891 Mr Morton's 'Hearts Ease' beat Mr Handley's 'Mountain Chief'. His fortunes zoomed again in 1893, however, when his aged bull 'St Clair' beat Mr Atkinson's bull which had won second but Mr Atkinson got his revenge the next year when he beat the Handley entry in the aged bull and bull calf class.

1894 was William's last show and in 1895 the *Gazette* reporter was already looking back 'to the great days when the cattle ring was dominated by the late John Morton and William Handley'. William Handley was not to be forgotten as the Society's first Memorial Trophy was named after him and, equally appropriately, his son John Handley won at the 1895 show with his bull under two years of age and also got a first for heifers not exceeding three years of age. John Handley never quite enjoyed the success let lone the supremacy of his father but he did well enough. Moreover he continued to obtain his stock from the highest sources and in 1896 obtained 'Leonard, bred by Her Majesty The Queen'. Humiliatingly 'Leonard' came second to Mr J. Rook's 'Duke of Fife' in aged bulls but the third winner was also out of a Handley bull 'Cock of the North'.

'Leonard' got the Championship in 1897 but was not entered in 1898 when the winning aged bull 'Prince of the North' again came from Greenhead.

That there was an over concentration on the 'bull market' was shown by the relative insignificance of dairy cattle at the show especially in the 1880's. In 1887 there were only three entries for cows in milk and the 'falling off' was attributed to the 'cruelty to animals people' who objected to 'big bags'. Five years later big bags were still noticeable but the dairy quality had improved so that breeders 'from away' were warned 'that a good cow at home is but a laughing stock in Kendal'.

As it neared its Centenary the Society re-emphasised its objective to encourage all farmers and in 1896 allowed the *Westmorland Gazette* to present a prize for 'smaller farmers' showing one agricultural horse, one cow and one yearling beast. Once more the emphasis was noticeably on cattle rather than on other animals including sheep.

Strangely sheep at Kendal, whose town motto was generally translated as being 'Wool is our bread', occupied a lowly position in general classes and were not numerous in the specialised sections at the show. Wool was actually displayed at the show but was never given much prominence. Thus in 1846 as against 87 entries for cattle there were only 'fifty for sheep and wool'. The class then seems to have been dropped for in 1855 'the mayor [who was in fact the Society's secretary William Longmire] adverting to the intimate connection of the manufacturers of Kendal to the agricultural interest reminded them (the company at dinner) that formerly a prize for wool was given by the Society. This should be re-established but not as formerly for quantity but it should be for the whole clip'. He observed that wool quality was improving although it was still variable: 'There was wool worth 8s 6d which was formerly worth 6s and all grown

on the same farm'. Thereafter samples were exhibited and in 1880 there was an 'exhibition of the wool of all nations...but...the attendance was poor'. A similar sorry verdict was given to the 1882 Wool Show although Lady Bective had offered £5 for 'the best local fleece'. Nevertheless there were twelve entries for the wool classes in 1883 from many leading farmers including W. Dobson of Sellet Hall with his

A rare Herdwick champion ram 'Nero'

Leicesters, E. Moorhouse of Natland-Shrop-shires, R. Parker, Moss End, Horned Cragg and F.G. Tyson Kentmere and R. Bownass of Middleton Hall with Westmorland Black Faced. There was a noisy dispute after two long woolled fleeces entered by I. Jackson of Yealand were alleged not to be genuinely pure Leicesters. Whether or not this row set the seal on the competition or whether it was simply on account of low entries there were no more references to a Wool Show in succeeding years.

On the field there were always relatively few sheep. Only 29 were entered for seven classes in 1850. In 1851 entries rose to 103 and the following year the section was extended to include Leicesters, Southdowns and Fell Sheep in a variety of classes including best shearling rams, best three-toothed gimmers, best five ewes, best two lambs and three gimmer lambs. Nevertheless sheep 'dropped' again and there were only about 50 entries in 1855 and in 1857 they were well down.

Inevitably the prize winners for sheep were widely spread in accordance with the suitability of the varieties to the differing geographical characteristics of the district. The Southdown winner was frequently the Hon. Mrs Mary Howard and her successor General Arthur Upton at Levens Hall; the Leicesters championship was long held by the Browne family of Troutbeck while Shropshires won for many farmers of lower land who included William Handley, at that time

Champion Herdwick ram 'Lord Paramount' with R.W. Hawell of Threlkeld 1882

at Low Bleaze, in 1863.

The 1870's and 1880's were the worst years for sheep at the show. In 1871 there were 'good entries but no new developments'; in 1876 there were only seven entries for fell sheep and the largest entry was only ten for aged Leicesters. In 1877 six were entered for the fell sheep classes but there were twelve in the Leicester tup lambs class where all three prizes were taken by Messrs Cock of Coat Green, Dalton (Burton-in-Kendal). Mr J. Cock won again in 1879 with a 'wonderfully pure bred ram' and along with Mr W. Dobson of Sellet Hall 'swept the board' with Leicesters for the next few years.

Longwoolled breeds were championed by Mr W.H. Wakefield of Sedgwick House with Shropshires and the Earl of Lonsdale with Downlands which apparently did well on the Earl's Shap fell uplands.

'Real' fell sheep were all but absent from the show. In 1882 Mr Atkinson of Old Oak, Windermere was the only exhibitor of Herdwicks. Nevertheless, in the same year Garnett's Westmorland Agriculture gave prominence to R.W. Hawell of Threlkeld's champion Herdwick ram 'Lord Paramount'.

Longwoolled sheep remained the most popular. 'One expects nothing short of perfection in such veteran breeders as Messrs Dobson, Cock and Co' eulogised the *Gazette* in 1885 although the aged ram champion was Mr W. Wilson of Castle Meadows. A few Blue Faced were exhibited by Mr R. Capstick in 1889 and partly as a result new classes were recommended. Wensleydales appeared at the 1890 show when 'Mr Rhodes of Westhouse exhibit showed superiority over all other breeds'! There were also 16 entries for tup lambs 'the like of which had been sold for £8 10s'. The longwoolled breeders like Mr Dargue of Burneside Hall (who began a notable showing career in the early 1890s), Henry Cock of Coat Green and William Dobson of Sellet Hall and Mr Thompson of Singleton Park would have disagreed. Even so they themselves experimented with fell sheep and in 1891 Mr Dargue came second to 'Bobby' Rawlinson with Scotch Black Faced. In the same year John Rigg of Windermere and John Dove of Ambleside had a 'good lot of winners' in Herdwicks. Though the *Gazette* grumbled that Rough Fell sheep were 'undoubtedly rough and are not the kind of sheep to add to the beauty of the Show...it is necessary in a fell district that a class should be formed for them'.

The Wensleydales' popularity grew quickly with 36 entries in 1893 when 'there was only one judge as the other did not turn up which is far too much for one judge'. In 1894 there were 41 entries from 15 exhibitors all of whom came from the Kirkby Lonsdale and Sedbergh areas. The old Scotch Black Faced still held their own, however, and Mr Dargue won five firsts at the same show. Wensleydales were again well to the fore in 1898 when Leicesters were withdrawn as the last remaining exhibitor Mr Dobson had died and Mr Cock of Coat Green had retired. Hence forward Leicesters would be amalgamated with other longwoolled varieties, a clear sign that with regard to sheep times were changing.

Horses, surprisingly, for a hilly area with few mounted hunts, invariably attracted as many entries as for sheep while for the average spectator they were always the most popular animals especially after the gymkhanas known as 'leaping competitions' were introduced. In the early years the Society's specialist shows inevitably drew away support from the horse classes in the main autumn show. Even so there were 42 horses compared to 50 sheep and wool entries at the 1846 show and 32 for horses compared to 29 sheep at the 1850 show. Little or no attention seems to have been paid as yet to agricultural horses and the 1850 report stressed the hunter's classes for one year old colts and fillies, two year olds, three year olds and so on. In 1855 there was a good entry especially from the 'progeny of Collingwood' which the Society had sponsored at stud during the previous two years. Eventually in 1857, when there were already ten classes for the mixed 'road and field' horses, two classes for agricultural horses were started. The prizes included a premium from Mr W. Ellison junior for the best filly or colt from his horse 'Sizergh' and in all there were 109 entries. By 1857 when there were 136 entries the report was able to boast there 'was a fine show of horses which has become a leading feature of the Society's exhibition'. Over the next decade interest in local breeding grew and in 1869 the winners in the best colt foal class were W.H. Wakefield, Richard Ormerod of Ackenthwaite House, James Breaks of Kendal, with George Hudson of Longsleddale highly commended. Entries continued to rise and in 1871 there were eleven entries for one year old geldings, nine for two year olds, eleven for three year olds, twenty-two for brood mares, and eighteen for filly in foal. Similarly in 1876 there were twenty classes 'and not one class badly filled'. The highest overall entries were thirty in the road or field classes but there were seven for geldings or fillies and eight for brood mares in the agricultural classes, twenty-one for hackneys and, interestingly for future developments, eight for ponies. Contradicting previous policy there were calls that the 'bred in the district' classes should be abandoned as it prevented local breeders having an external standard to aim at and 'so discouraged future improvement'.

It was in the late seventies that Mr T. Dixon of Dalton Old Hall, Burton-in-Kendal emerged as a notable horse breeder who almost rivalled the esteem won in Shorthorns by William Handley. In 1878 he won the roadster class and, with his 'May Fly' the two year old class and, in the over used *Gazette* phrase of the period, he all but 'swept the board' in 1880. The exception was for 'best four year old for road or field not more than fifteen hands two inches high' for which a 'barometer worth three guineas' was won by J. Metcalf. One of Mr Dixon's 'important' winners was a two year old gelding 'Loaf Sugar' which had won previously at the Royal. A similar gelding 'a chestnut moving straight and well

A pair of 'lighter heavies' ploughing a fellside furrow

with excellent shoulders, legs and length' won for him in 1881. In 1881 the main honours went respectively to Mr Nelson of Scotforth and Mr Abbot of Kirkby Lonsdale and in 1884 a large entry of seventeen in the hackney class was won by W. Thompson of Moresdale Hall. But in 1884 Mr Dixon's stable was still on form for he won the best Brood Mare class which had attracted eight entries. A carping note crept into the 1885 report for 'in hackneys everything was shown from the thick set harness pony to the 'black cobber' or 'Sandside hack'. The winning hackney horse was 'Lady Watson' (belonging to G.W. Wilson of Rigmaden) who 'has come out again after being at stud fresher and better than ever'. Moreover, she beat the fancied favourite from G.E. Wilson's Dallam Tower stable. Mr Dixon continued to do well and, for instance, he won the yearling fillies class in 1888 and his three year old filly 'Laughing Stock' won in 1893. Some of his rivals did well enough. In 1888 the finest brood mare was 'Tarnwater' which belonged to Mr W. Nelson. In 1891 Mr Dixon's colt was 'beaten by an outsider a very neat horse' belonging to Mr Kidd of Haverflatts, Milnthorpe. Only in the mid nineties was Mr Dixon eclipsed by other breeders none of whom was as consistently successful. Thus in 'light brood mare hunters' - in 1896 - A. Orr's 'Bondmaid', which had won one hundred firsts, was beaten by C.H. Wilson's 'Charlotte' leaving 'the crowd to ponder that it all depends on the judges'.

Agricultural horses which became a spectacular feature of early twentieth century shows gradually came to the fore from the 1870's onwards. In 1876 there were only seven entries in the filly or gelding agricultural class and, though numbers did not improve for a long time, some winners like a three year old filly belonging to Mr James Woof of Great Strickland Mills were given as much publicity as hackneys. Continuing the family tradition of encouraging farming (as distinct from recreational riding) Mrs Wilson of Dallam Tower presented a prize during the 1880's for the best work horses. The earlier prize winners in this class tended to come from just outside the county until in 1888 the Clement family - R. Clement of Levens and T. Clement of Underbarrow - began to win with their horses. Over the next ten years they were frequently the champions though in 1896 Mr T. Clement's 'Lady Britannia' which 'has won 23 first prizes and two cups' was beaten by Mr P. Gregson's 'Shire Pride' of Lancaster. The excuse was that 'Lady Britannia' 'was a little out of condition and her foal had gravel in its feet'. An equally outstanding horse at this time was 'Lady Coram' who belonged to the Reich family. They were among the first to introduce the pure Clydesdale horses to the Kendal ring. Their greatest success was probably in 1897 when their brood mares 'Miss Warden' and 'Miss Goram' beat Victor Cavendish's 'Holker Maud' for the main medal. Moreover, in 1897, the future success of the horse classes seemed assured as entries had risen to 148 from 99 in 1896 in the agricultural classes and to 226 from 199 for light horses.

The rise in popularity of the horse classes towards the end of the Society's first century was the first indication that the annual show in addition to being a trade exhibition for busy professionals could also provide something for the non-farming masses - namely entertainment. In this sphere by far the biggest attraction was 'Show Jumping'. A class for 'Hunters to leap over hurdles' was first introduced in 1863. Though the prizes at £10 and £5 were considered by some committee members to be too high the event had an immediate effect on gate money which rose from £31 in 1862 to £50. By later standards the 'jumps' were tame affairs as, in 1867, the course ran 'between two lines of sheep pens and crossed by three hurdles topped by furze'. The 1867 winner was 'a fine animal belonging to Mr W. Wakefield and ridden by a boy (unnamed) of twelve or thirteen who is the son of Mr Wakefield's coachman and rode without stirrups...beside getting what might be called golden opinions the boy got something more substantial in the shape of a half sovereign which was given by a lady who was present'. A novel feature at the same show was a 'shoeing competition' for a prize given by Mr Eastcott, veterinary surgeon of Kendal, the successful sons of Vulcan being Mr T. Unsworth, Kendal and Mr R. Gibson of Beetham. By 1871 the Grandstands which 'were full of ladies' were stationed specifically to get the best view of the leaping and from 1874 the 'names and colours of the entrants as shown by ribbons' were entered in the catalogue.

After several good years with crowds of several thousand watching what to the general public was the final event of show day, there had been some falling off of interest and in 1868 it was reported that horses in general were 'not up to the quality they should be...and...the hurdle leaping was indifferent'. In 1877 there was a 'low turn out for the leaping on account of the harvest and Princess Louise being in Carlisle'. Attendance was still down in 1880 but in 1883 'The Leapers' earned a separate sub heading in the report when 'the winner 'Rocco' moved beautifully and is the model of a light weight hunter' as ridden by Mr Wilson to beat Mr Tyson's 'Brief Bliss' and Mr Wilson's 'Star'. A water jump was added to the course in 1885 and the *Gazette* reported that some of the best jumping 'ever seen' (!) had occurred. Almost all the leading riders, at this stage, came from out of the county and included Dr Iliffe of Yorkshire and W. Jagger of Wakefield who after a long drawn out jump off won in 1894. In 1897 there was a tie for first place shared by Mr Young of Carlisle and Mr R. Bownass of Bowness. Amongst other more local riders were W. Ruecastle of Bentham (second in 1894), Dr Jackson of Carnforth and Mr T. Hilton who rode for Mr James Wilson of Crosthwaite, who won in 1888 when 'during the whole leaping he did not make a single mistake and took the water in splendid form'.

Thrills and spills added to the allure of the event. Watched by a crowd of 4,000 one of the horses after knocking down the drystone wall jump ran into the crowd 'knocking three or four people over but fortunately no one was hurt'. During the final 'jump off' in 1896 'Dr Jackson's horse caught its forelegs in the fence wall and turned a complete summersault and its rider Hayton came a nasty cropper as the horse rolled on him but he was no worse beyond a severe shaking'. This mishap led to complaints 'that judges were allowing two horses to leap at the same time to the danger of horse and rider'. Accordingly the final jumps over the four fences had to be taken individually in future but this slowed everything down. The next year was particularly bad: 'The leaping which should have started at 3.30 didn't until 5 o'clock so it was almost dark before the final and most of the crowd had gone home.'

One of the reasons for the late start to the 1897 leaping was the delay caused earlier on by the speechifying in the president's luncheon tent. Wining, dining and speech making at the show were always reported as fully as were the cattle sections and, no doubt in return for a free dinner, the substance of the hospitality was lavishly extolled by the reporter. Until 1877 the banquet took the form of an after show dinner. Thus in 1847 Mr Alderman Thompson presided at a sumptuous feast provided by Mr Fisher of the Commercial Hotel in the Whitehall (later the Town Hall) Assembly Room. As in 1850 when the 'dinner was provided in as liberal a manner and excellent style for which Mr Jackson's establishment is noted' the usual venue in the earlier years was The King's Arms. In 1855 the Commercial Hotel again did the catering in the Whitehall where 'there was a sufficient corps of waiters who put everything within reach of the guests, a point which most who have been accustomed to attend large public dinners will not be inclined to think of as secondary moment'. A change occurred again in 1862 when 'between one and two hundred of the gentry and leading agriculturists' partook of 'every delicacy of the season' provided by Mr and Mrs Dixon of the Crown Hotel.

Drink was as important as food and the list of toasts often neared twenty. In the 1850's they included 'The Queen, Prince Albert, The Royal Family, The Lord Lieutenant - Lord Lonsdale, The Army and The Navy, The Members for the County and Borough, The Landed Proprietors, The Successful and Unsuccessful Exhibitors, The Clergy of the Dioceses (until the 1860's half the county was in the Diocese of Chester and the other half in Carlisle but there was only one toast), The Bonnie Lasses of Westmorland (none of whom were allowed to attend) and the High Sheriff.'

Each toast was preceded by a speech which often touched on the politics of the day. In 1854 just as the Crimean War was breaking out 'the Earl of Bective who presided in the absence of the High Sheriff felt confident that we should see peace restored and on a firmer and surer footing... He felt sorry that he could not discuss agricultural subjects with them but they might rest assured that he felt a warm interest in the welfare of the county and of the Kendal Agricultural Society'. Such sentiments were hardly surprising as he was one of the MP's and the Society's principal patron! A rarer note was struck in the tributes to our French allies in 1855 when Colonel Upton 'after the toast to the Queen proposed that of the Emperor and Empress of the French. No one had more confidence in the address, in the resolution and in the honesty of the Emperor of the French (renewed cheers)'. Times changed, however, and with the war won in the Crimea Emperor Napoleon III's threatening of British interests led to the creation of a part time army of Volunteers who, of course, had to be toasted at the show. Thus in 1861 Captain Whitwell in proposing the toast 'hoped that they might not be called upon for actual service but the movement...would...intimidate those who might have hostile intentions against our homesteads and families'. Moreover in a complete reversal of all previous opinions Richard Cobden, the reviled 'architect of Free Trade' of a decade earlier, was hailed 'as a great patriot' who would see that 'whenever the French Emperor built one ship we should build two'. In 1876 at the time of 'The Bulgarian Horrors' the toast was to 'the Christians in the East' which probably did little to cheer the company who that year partook of a mere 'cold collation' served in the Town Hall.

The next year the venue and repast were changed to a luncheon at three shillings a head in a marquee on the show field to which 'ladies were admitted' for the first time. This change also resulted in a reduction in the number of toasts and, therefore, of speeches.

'Let the grumblers grumble' was one verdict, 'even a short speech under an umbrella is better than long ones in a banqueting room'. Deserved grumbles resulted a year later when the marquee blew down and a depleted party of only a hundred had to have a makeshift meal in the Market Hall half a mile from the field. As a result of this disaster in 1878 the Society reverted to a dinner at the Commercial Hotel though with the unusual absence of both the MP and the Mayor of Kendal it was not a notable occasion. The Earl of Bective, however, hit the headlines by denouncing the inadequacy of the cattle disease regulations. He 'spoke of how after a cargo of diseased stock had been detected at Barrow Docks the wooded scantlings (*sic*) used to pen the animals on board had been sold in the Furness area'. No doubt in an attempt to lighten the tone of the dinners a 'Musical Concert' was arranged in 1882 by Lady Bective, Mrs Wilson and Mrs Wakefield in St. George's Hall where the feast was served but the experiment was not repeated. The Society preferred speeches to the 'great and wonderful gift of God' and in 1883 dinner was served by Mr and Mrs Lancaster at the Commercial Hotel where venison, the gift of Lord Lonsdale, was on the menu. Braving the elements once more the Society returned permanently, despite the occasional gale, to a marquee on the field in 1884 where luncheon was provided by Mr James Bell of The King's Arms at 4.30pm. A more normal lunchtime - though two hours later than farmhouse dinner - of 2pm was the chosen time in 1887 when two hundred members and guests toasted Captain and Mrs Bagot on undertaking 'the lottery of marriage.' The Captain, subsequently the Member of Parliament and ultimately Sir Josceline, graced almost all the shows until his death in 1913. At the 1898 luncheon he considered that transport was the main problem for Westmorland agriculture and, accordingly, he was pleased that a light railway was being planned to run between Kirkby Lonsdale and Kendal. Above all, however, he was satisfied that the show and the Society, as the centenary of their foundation approached in 1899, were still being run on the right lines.

CHAPTER FOUR

Old and New 1899-1940

The Kendal Agricultural Society's first hundred years had coincided with the peak of British power and economic importance. Throughout the nineteenth century Britain was the strongest and richest nation on earth. Britannia ruled the waves, the bounds of the British Empire, covering a quarter

Above: Shorthorn Society medal awarded at the 1921 show to W. Woof of Clawthorpe Hall, Burton in Kendal

Below: Reflecting their era. Shorthorn calves 1899

Lord and Lady Henry Bentinck

of the earth's surface, were still spreading and we were the Workshop of the World. By 1899 'Free trade' corn had provided the urban masses with three quarters of their bread for over fifty years but, fortunately for Westmorland's stock farmers and shepherds, most of the rest of the country's food was culled from British soil. Agriculture with a million workers remained our largest industry. To all appearances the landed interest still pulled on the reins of power. The presence of the 'county' set at the County Show still seemed to demonstrate that the upper classes had the upper hand. All reports throughout the period gave prominence to the 'Gentry' who attended. A typical year was 1903 when the prize giving ceremony was graced by the presence of Lord and Lady Henry Bentinck, Captain Bagot MP, Sir Joseph and Lady Savory, Mrs. C.J. and the Hon. Mrs. Cropper, Mr and Mrs. F.W. Crewdson, Major J.G. Gandy and Gerald Garnett esq. Thirty years later most of the same families were still present. In the various photographs of the presidential party the central figure, clad progressively in flowing late Victorian garb through to the short skirted flapper styles of the twenties and on to the high heeled svelte forms of the late 1930's, always seems to have been Lady Henry Bentinck, chatelaine of Underley Hall. Her Ladyship when off the hunting field invariably dressed at the pinnacle of fashion. Other show patrons, especially the men, were more conservative. Top hats were still worn around the president's tent up to 1913 and as late as 1935 a crowd photograph shows everyone either capped or felt, straw or bowler hatted. White coats were first worn in the ring in c.1931 but the 1936 photographs show several stockmen in gaiters.

In 1931, however, the *Westmorland Gazette* with Edwardian unctuousness sang the praises not of Lady Henry but of 'Lord Henry Bentinck the Society's president...which...is extremely fortunate. To have for its patron not merely a figurehead but one whose name stands for Sterling (a topical reference as Britain had just left the gold standard) in the agricultural world is a big asset. The (show) president this year is the High Sheriff Mr A.H. Willink whose interest in

Edwardian gentry survey the show Photo: Margaret Duff Collection

the welfare of the county is by no means confined to music and festival matters. Once more Mr Jacob Wakefield is the treasurer and Mr Punchard (Lord Henry's agent) was the courteous secretary'. Any losses in the ranks of the gentry but not from among farmers or exhibitors were invariably mentioned. Thus there were flowery tributes in 1913 to Sir Josceline Bagot MP 'the beau ideal of a country member' and in 1926 to Sir John Weston MP who 'had set the rare example of reducing speech making to a minimum of words with the maximum of cheerfulness'. Though they had the interests of the land at heart few of the apparent squires lording it in the President's tent were entirely dependent on the land. Great landlords like the Bentincks and the Bagots of Levens were outbalanced in the county hierarchy by plutocrats whose wealth largely derived from non-agricultural sources. Thus in the select gathering of 1903 the Wakefields and Gandys had banking and gunpowder interests and Colonel Weston ran the gunpowder works. Throughout the period it was customary for the High Sheriff of the County to be the President of the show. Their ranks reflected the mixed economy of the nation just as the fondness of many Sheriffs for military titles, earned for the most part in peacetime or auxiliary service rather than on the field of battle, stressed the war torn nature of the first half of the twentieth century. Only two show presidents - Victor Cavendish of Holker, later eighth Duke of Devonshire, Sheriff and President in 1900, and Lord Hothfield of Appleby Castle in 1903 - were lords of great estates. Many, however, were substantial squires including Colonel Bordrigge North North [yes! this really was his name] of Thurland - 1907, Captain Bagot - 1911, Lt. Col. Fothergill of Ravenstonedale

- 1922 and Major E.W. Hassell of Dalemain - 1927. In 1935 Mr F.J. Milne, Broad Leys, Windermere held the dual honour. He was a 'well known sports man who has shot and fished in every quarter of the globe...it was also fitting that an athlete who some years ago distinguished himself in Lancashire and the north of England Rugby football should find himself at home on the playing ground of England's most successful Rugby club of last year'. Like Milne several Lake District Presidents including Richard Rigg of Applegarth - 1906 - and G.H. Pattinson of Windermere - 1921 - also had mixed commercial and landed interests while Charles J. Cropper - 1905 - paper manufacturer of Burneside, R.D. Holt of Blackwell, Winster, a Blackburn brewer - 1923 - and Jacob Wakefield - 1929 - Sedgwick gunpowder, were industrialists. Other leading industrialists like Sir Samuel Scott Bart., founder of the Kendal based Provincial Insurance Company and also the owner of mills in Bolton, actively supported Westmorland agriculture. Their farming activities were, however, more likely to be a drain on their wealth than a contributor to it.

As for the farmers who ran the show they had no alternative but to carry on weathering the fluctuations in markets which apart from the boom war years were invariably depressed. Nevertheless almost all the old farming families survived and their stolidity is mirrored in the long service on the show committees of many members. They included R. Cottam, Skelsmergh, J. Dargue of Burneside Hall, H. Dobinson, Helsington, William Dobson, Sellet Hall, J. Gibson, Ings, two J. Handleys, uncle and nephew respectively, of Greenhead and Heversham Hall, J. Hudson, Orrest, R. Mashiter, Deepthwaite, G. Proctor, Low Bleaze, T. Robinson, Holmescales, W. Richardson, Laverock Bridge and W. Woof of Clawthorpe.

Equally enduring were the show Secretaries. Only in 1919 was Mr G.L. Hoggarth, 'the veteran secretary of the Show', replaced after 35 years by Mr G.E. Thompson who received a salary of £40 pa. After Mr Thompson's resignation 'was accepted with regret in 1928' Mr G. Punchard was appointed - out of eleven applicants - at a salary of £60. Despite courteous references to his courtesy he seems to have been a disaster. Show entries declined during his secretaryship while the minute books kept by Punchard are so illegible and blotched as to make them virtually useless as a historical record. When he resigned in 1935 Sir Samuel Scott in accepting the resignation expressed only scanty thanks for his services but added 'if you feel that this record should be worded in any other way, will you kindly let me know so that we can consider it'. Punchard was followed as secretary by Michael Hodgson, of the famous auctioneer family, who was much more successful and, incidentally, legible. All the Society's and show records were hand written up to the 1940's perhaps signifying the strength of holding on to tradition. Time and time again after 1919 the survival of old ways such as the use of agricultural horses was given as much emphasis in reports as was given to mechanical and other innovations. When it came to a choice between old and new the Westmorland farmers as represented at the show seem to have preferred the old.

Literally hitting an old-fashioned note was the repertoire of the Kendal Borough band. First engaged for the Centenary celebrations at a fee of £10 which was increased in 1910 to £12 providing that there were '20 instruments to be played until 4.30pm' the band played on into the 1920's and 1930's when they received £30 and played until 5pm. But the same old tunes were wafted out and in 1931, for instance, the band master Mr R.E. Allan conducted such Edwardian gems as 'selections of Schubert, Pirates of Penzance, Poetic Fancies' and - a little more modern - 'Lilac Time'. In 1936 a public address system with echoing loudspeakers was introduced to announce events and prize winners but it was not until after the Second World War that any 'canned' music was allowed.

Twenty years earlier as the old century made way for the new no one needed such cosy reassurance that things had not changed all that much. Happily for the Centenary show neither the best nor the worst of what was to come was envisaged by anybody. Just as the crowds watching, in 1897, the Diamond Jubilee procession of Queen Victoria must have thought that such Imperial splendour was everlasting, so their rural cousins two years later, thronging to Longlands on an appropriately 'bright and breezy' day for the Centenary show might well have imagined that the land in every sense was in good shape. As regards local memory Victoria's national event and the show's local celebration were fused in time and several accounts in the 1920's and 1930's of the show's history refer to the 'Centenary Show of 1897'.

The Longlands venue rented from Messrs Maudsley of Spital Farm for £15 was described as being 'between the Skelsmergh and Grayrigg roads about 5 minutes walk from the station'. Moreover, the new field meant 'that both exhibitors and spectators had much more room to spread than on the old ground behind the station'. Most of the patrons still came to the show by train. Special excursions were run from Lancaster, Skipton and Kirkby Stephen. Following complaints of delays of over two hours it was resolved in 1908 'to ask Mr Wakefield to see Mr Cropper, a director of the L&NW railway' to do something about the problem.

Though the Society did not own the field it embarked on several capital improvements to walls and gates. In 1925 new entrance gates were made nearer together than formerly to do away with previous arrangements whereby, according to one bystander it had 'tacken hoaf a dozen fwoak ta bring yan epp in t' field'. Earlier in 1906 the field committee, at a cost of £321, had engaged Pattinson's to erect a galvanised storage shed 35 x 30ft. and three grandstands 50 x 21 x 8ft. The latter were furnished with 'three planks for seats planed both sides' ranged in two stands in six tiers and in the third in four. Strangely there are no reports or references in the minutes as to the sanitary arrangements made to cope with the needs of several thousand people. For the relief of those who had taken copious refreshment in the beer tent there would have been the noxious and traditional hessian screen up against the back hedge but this would not have been an adequate convenience for ladies.

The show stayed at Longlands for a whole generation until 1935 when after repeated disputes with the landlords who, for instance, had demanded higher rent if it rained, it was decided to go elsewhere. Two fields belonging respectively to Mr Moffat and Mr Beck on offer at £30 were rejected in favour of the Kendal Rugby Union Football ground at Mintsfeet for which the rent was £27. As the Society still retained its old shed at Longlands for which it paid a ground rent of £3 it was not financially better off especially as the rugger field was smaller and the income from parking was reduced. Hence in 1938 the show returned to Longlands. Though the rent was now £40 everyone thought the restored arrangements were 'admirable for the purpose.'

Congratulations and self praise were always in order in both the media and the Society's reports. The same records also trace the gradual change by which what had originally been entitled the 'Kendal Show' became the more high faluting 'County Show'. Thus the 1901 Westmorland Society's Show was 'one of the best one day's shows in the north of England with the exception of Altringham'; the 1907 was 'the best in the north of England excluding of course the Great Yorkshire and the Royal Lancashire' while in 1926 'the famous Westmorland County Show...concedes first place to no other one-day show....'.

Hopes and opinions were never higher than in 1899 when no effort was spared to ensure that the Centenary Show was the best yet. After 'a long discussion' it had been decided that there should be more prizes 'except for pigs' and that there should be special Silver Centenary medals for all 'except Hen

Eggs'. Accordingly 100 medals 'at £33 in cases complete' were ordered from Mr Rhodes jeweller of Highgate who also 'gratuitously' displayed some of the Society's oldest trophies in his shop window for a week before the show. A variation on convivial arrangements was that the traditional 'set and sit down

Special Centenary medal presented by the Westmorland Gazette to John Handley of Green Head for best male shorthorn 'Lord James Douglas'

dinner' at noon was to be replaced by a running luncheon from 12 to 2 and 'the Hotel caterers be asked to provide seperate' (*sic*) tables and also a tent for tea and coffee and temperance drinks. Free non temperance drinks were to be limited and to deter gate crashers a portion of the tent should be screened off and bear a notice 'No admission except for judges and committee to this portion of the tent'. To prevent passers by getting a free look the committee also screened the roadsides with 400 yards of canvas costing £5 which may have contributed a little to the crowd exceeding 5,000, the largest so far recorded. This figure was only exceeded in 1920 and in 1925 when it was estimated that there were 7,000 in the crowd.

The Centenary Show had the best ever number of entries with 1,178 as against the previous best of 978 in Jubilee year 1897 and the next best of 999 in 1912. The 1904 show earned particularly high praises for 'Mr G.L. Hoggarth's arrangements are generally speaking excellent and notwithstanding the fact that there was a counter attraction in the shape of Buffalo Bill's Wild West Show on the other side of the road. Mr Hodgson was assisted by the field committee led by Mr Thos. Geldert...though he just contrives to whip his own top'. Other good years with high entries between 1899 and 1913 were 988 in 1903 and 963 in 1909.

The Great War broke out six weeks before the date of the planned 1914 show. Although the conflict was expected to be over by Christmas the committee only four days after the declaration minuted 'it was proposed by Mr T.B. Punchard and seconded by Mr T. Morton and carried unanimously that owing to the War the show of this Society be abandoned for this year'. All subscriptions would be 'credited to the 1915 show'. The 1915 Easter show of 'entire horses' went ahead as usual on the New Road in Kendal and it was only after a long debate that it was voted by 10 to 5 not to hold a show in 1915.

Though the next show had to wait until after 'war to end all wars' was over the Society, nevertheless, continued to meet and contributed to the war effort. In February 1915 Mr Wakefield went as the Westmorland delegate to a conference in London about 're-instatement of land in Belgium and France after the War'. £300 of the Society's reserves were invested in Exchequer Bonds and £100 was donated to 'Agriculture in the countries of our allies' to which the secretary Mr Hoggarth donated £10 of his salary. In 1916 the Society successfully resisted the demands of the military to requisition its equipment shed.

The most controversial wartime venture was the decision made in 1917 by 18 votes to 12 to buy a threshing machine which would tour the farms of members in the months after harvest. In the event the machine was never fully utilised and as soon as the war was over it was decided to sell it for £200.

The first postwar show in 1919 was considered to be a great success and earned headlines 'The County Show: Notable Exhibition in Bad Weather, Five

Threshing day c.1914

A pre-first world war tractor

thousand watch jumping'. Entries were down to 685 compared to 960 in 1913. The biggest drop was in cattle, down from 161 to a mere 58 reflecting the wartime switch to arable cultivation. Because of increased ploughing Heavy Horse entries at 116 were almost at the 1913 figure of 121 and, indeed, exceeded the 1910 entry of 110. Although tractor ploughs had been first introduced in Westmorland on Garnett's farm at Ackenthwaite in 1915 and there were said to be a dozen tractors in the Milnthorpe area by 1918 horses still ruled the ploughlands of North Westmorland and Lunesdale. In 1920 the *Gazette* reporting on the trade section at the show noted that 'there were no new mechanical implements on view in the field which is a matter for surprise as there are many types of motor plough on the market which in addition to ploughing perform a hundred and one other things...' Motorised farming had to wait another 20 years until the next reign of 'War Ag.' brought in the grey Fordsons.

Despite good attendances in the early twenties and at £650 in 1926 the highest prize money of any other northern one day show, none of the interwar shows recovered their pre-1914 popularity. The highest number of entries between 1919 and 1938 were 904 in 1925 and 962 in Coronation year 1937. The latter figure was an upturn on the average number of entries for the inter-war years which generally hovered around the 800's with a 'rock bottom' year in 1934 when there were only 661 entries and 'the gate' was 'down by £60 despite butter-melting weather' to £265 12s 6d.

As in so much else the 1899 show was the benchmark by which receipts from later shows were judged. The Centenary Show's total receipts amounted to £391 as against £237 in 1898 and £193 in 1897. The 1899 figure included £80 for 4s seats in a new grandstand and £27 for catalogues. 1900 saw a predictable drop in income to £307 and with the exception of 1903 when receipts peaked at £455 the income for most of the pre First World War shows fell and reached the lowest point with £237 in 1909. Even in 1909, however, 4,544 shilling entrance tickets were sold. The first peacetime show of 1919 was hailed - inaccurately - as having attracted the highest ever attendance of 5,000. On this occasion £487 were taken but 'it must be borne in mind that charges were 50% higher than before the war'. 1920 brought 6,000 spectators producing £587. Thereafter revenue fell to such an extent that when the gate went up £105 to £293 in 1938 it was headline news in the *Gazette*. In the late 1930's prices of admission were: 'Adults before 4pm 1/6; between 4 and 6pm 1/-; Grandstands - covered 2/-; Open 1/-. Children half price; Cars on field 5/-'. Cars had first been allowed in 1920 when the fee was 10/- which in the values of 1999 was equivalent to £20! Entry fees were fixed at 7% of the first prize for the class and as prizes did not go up much there was no significant change in income from this source. Incredibly the Society's minimum subscription of five shillings first set in 1799 still applied and carried with it free admission to the show field. Faced with a decline in popularity, ageing committee members reluctant to change and a run of wet shows the Society's formerly healthy assets halved from £1140 in 1926 to £500 in 1931. Some minor and often counter-productive or footling economies like saving £7 by not hiring a special tent for the Women's Institutes and reducing the size of the medals were tried. It was not, however, until young blood including a new secretary Michael Hodgson came in during the late 1930's along with three fine show days in a row that financial matters improved.

Economic depression and higher entrance charges had much less effect on the show's popularity compared to Westmorland's most intractable obstacle: the weather. Following the lovely 'Queen's weather' of the Centenary Show in 1899 the weather in 1900 was 'on a par early on though the sky was grey and threatening but rain began falling at 4 o'clock just before the leapers'. 1901 was worse: 'heavy clouds packed around...and rain began to fall before the Show opened and fell pitilessly throughout the greater part of the day'. There followed a run of good years being 'a bright and mild morning but in the afternoon the atmosphere thickened and the sun no longer shone' in 1903. 'A brilliant day and a splendid show' was the verdict for 1907 but in 1909 though 'there were large crowds...a heavy shower of rain kept the town's people away'. Meteorological matters continued to be mixed in the inter-war years. In 1919 'it rained from 11 o'clock to 3.39 (sic) with a violence which suggested thunder'. The 1922 show had a good day despite 'wretched weather with scarcely a fine day all summer'. The 1923 report was infused with the 'determination that has made the British what we are': Following 'a period of depression which it has to be admitted has not hit our local agriculturists as hard as their brothers in many parts of the kingdom' the crowds flocked to the 'Kendal Show'. 'Undaunted by a grim and foreboding morning with the mountain tops hidden in mist and driving showers they made their way through the various mountain passes by motor, dog cart and charabanc'. 1925 was a 'magnificent' day but in 1926 the President Major Hassell declared 'it was a most depressing day and it was just as depressing when travelling over Shap to see so much corn uncut. The show ground was...more fitted for ducks than for sheep'. A bigger catastrophe befell the ground in 1930 when 'heavy rain fell in the night and several marquees whose swollen guy ropes tore the pegs from the ground collapsed including the butter and eggs tent, the Women's Institute tent and the luncheon tent'. Rising fittingly to the occasion the WI ladies quickly decamped from the muddy and unpleasant land of the showfield and mounted a display of 223 competition entries in the Y.W.C.A. headquarters half a mile away; other displays and demonstrations were also staged in the Auction Mart buildings while the luncheon was held in the implement shed. Almost as compensation for 1930 the succeeding pre-war shows generally enjoyed 'ideal' weather.

Apart from the Westmorland summer the show had its share of accidents.

In 1921 a chauffeur driven Daimler Landaulette, belonging to Colonel C.E. Walker of Lindeth Fell, Bowness which was in a convoy of equally grand vehicles bringing genteel patrons to the show, knocked down and killed 8 year old William Robinson on Correction Hill. Less tragic and more ludicrous were the attempts to introduce hound trailing. In 1931 the puppy event was declared invalid as all the dogs finished five seconds under the minimum time. Possibly they had been diverted by a simultaneous display by the Oxenholme Staghounds, accompanied by the master Miss Freda Weston and her scarlet coated huntsman Simms, '- who charged round the ring - all well mounted and making a gallant show'. At the second (and last for several years) hound trail in 1934 'at the finish while the judges and catchers waited at the main entrance...hounds wandered in from various other entrances and no result was possible'. After a committee lasting nearly an hour the trail was declared void but the row continued on longer.

Hound trails and hunting packs were but two of many attempts to vary both the entertainment and the exhibits. In a bid to attract younger interest there was from the early 1930's a Young Farmers judging competition for a challenge shield donated by the *Westmorland Gazette*. The first Westmorland YFC had been founded at the instigation of Sir Samuel Scott at Windermere in c. 1931. During the thirties YFC's in the county grew in number and membership. In 1935 six teams from five YFC's competed and in 1937 there were 13 teams, the winner being 'one of the Windermere teams'. In 1938 there were 12 entries and top prizes were taken by both Kirkby Stephen teams. In his adjudication of the sheep judging the assessor Mr J.H. Faulder of Newton Rigg farm school pronounced that 'the teams contained a great deal of excellent material...but the

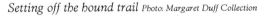

Setting off the hound trail Photo: Margaret Duff Collection

work of many of the competitors was rather spoiled through lack of training in giving verbal criticisms and reasons for arriving at decisions. They were rather apt to describe animals rather than comparing them and much improvement is required in forcefulness'.

Equestrian events as distinct from the show competition for horses were a feature of every show. Before 1914 there were displays of trotting and charging by the Cumberland and Westmorland Yeomanry. In the 1930's a children's gymkhana was introduced with such light hearted items as 'musical chairs, wheel barrow race, Polo Ballet and Potato race'. In 1938 a trick motor cyclist 'the Wizard on Wheels' was engaged but even then the main interest was always on the Show Jumping which rather quaintly was still called 'The Leapers'. At first there were only four jumps - 'easy fence, plain fence, stone wall and water jump' - but over the years their number and type increased to ensure that the leapers who always came on after 4pm rounded off show day with plenty of thrills and spills. Happily no accident to either riders or horses are recorded for the period.

In the early days, long before motorised horse boxes came in, there were relatively few entries. In 1902 the Kendal Show clashed with that at Bellingham and only five horses of poor quality appeared, 'one horse refusing eight times while the rest either just cleared or just failed to clear'. Despite £30 in prizes including £9 from the Oxenholme Hunt most of the competitors came from away. In 1904 there were entrants from Dumfries, Brailsford, Derbyshire, Nantwich, Stoke-on-Trent and Liverpool but not one local leaper. Five entrants withdrew out of 13 'thus', the *Gazette* helpfully calculated, 'reducing the number to eight'. Nevertheless the event attracted 'thousands' of spectators. F.W. Foster won the first prize of £15, while the second prize of £8 went to Great Ayton North Riding and the third of £4 went to Ormskirk. Post First World War shows continued to attract leapers of 'National Renown' - if not of The Grand National. The 1922 competitors included J. Taylor of Warrington who on 'Battleaxe' beat E. Bradley of Great Ayton's 'Spider' and G.&H. Taylor of Hornby's 'Springbok'. The following year, despite the turf being dried out in parts, there was 'grand leaping' over furze hurdle - one point, swing gate - three, in and out - three, imitation wall - three and water jump - six. M.C. Wellburn was the winner with 236 points to G. Dickinson of Cark's 226. In the late thirties a decline in entries for agricultural horses was counterbalanced by growing interest in 'hobby' horses. There were 23 entries for juvenile leaping in 1923 'which was of a very attractive character as the ground had dried up wonderfully after the early morning downpour... Mr A.H. Hindley added further laurels by annexing the juvenile leaping...young Sam Proctor was second and Mr H. Clark's pony was third.' There were 15 entrants in the Senior section in which 'Mr Joss Taylor of Warrington turned the tables on his close rival Mr T. Makin of Castleford' but 'a good day was had by all'.

Bridging the gap between rural entertainment and the full face of agriculture on display in the stock pens were the trade stands and demonstrations. Their popularity amongst show goers was always enhanced by generous hospitality on offer free. Messrs John Dockray of Kendal and Carnforth provided refreshment for 1,000 customers and friends in 1923. Until the late 1920's 'the stands' earned a separate paragraph in the press reports which reveal the gradual changes in the way of life in the Westmorland countryside. Even in 1899 mechanical innovations were highlighted. Amongst the displays of horse clothing by 'the Westmorland Woollen Company whose name always guarantees excellence' were 'Burman power clippers and sheep shearers: these attach to an india rubber tube and have a movable contrivance by which the teeth of the machine are readily applied in any direction on the animal's skin. The motion of the teeth is operated by a boy turning a handle'. In 1903 the most extensive exhibits were by Messrs E. Richardson and Co's 'range of churns, chaff cutters, mowers, reapers, sheep racks and troughs, sheep dipping apparatus etc'. The most popular display was, however, 'Mr H. Croft's range of cycles both of his own manufacture and by well known firms'. The motor age was still some time off and in 1906 Mr F.R. Bowness displayed his 'improved governess cart, luggage float and a horse-ralli (*sic*) car'. A lighter note was struck in 1904 by Messrs L. Airey and Co's stand which 'contained their well known Kendal acetylene generator - an instrument of great benefit to those in country districts where the oil lamp still prevails. One machine capable of lighting 400 25-candle power burners for six hours with one charge which has been purchased by a local gunpowder firm gave an excellent example of the benefits to be derived from this excellent power of illumination'. In case there were any risks in the home - let alone in a gunpowder works! - it was reported in 1906 'though fire extinguishing has not much in common with agricultural shows there were two demonstrations given by the Minimax Extinguisher in the field adjoining Longlands...the effect of the liquid used on the fire was almost instantaneous'. Other potential farmhouse artefacts on display included a stand, in 1912, of Messrs Singer's sewing machines and 'the Boras vacume carpet extractor, a most useful and effective article available at a low figure from the Stramongate depot'.

Horticulture first arrived at the show in the commercial section and in 1912 Clarence Webb of Kendal had a 'most noticeable display of gladioli and the new blue Saxony Dahlias along with some local apples and onions one of which weighed 3lbs.' Shifting the attention of the Westmerian show goers away from hearth and home was the 1909 stand of the 'British South Africa Company, showing the products of Rhodesia with a view to procuring settlers in...that colony'.

There were no trade stands at the 1919 show as 'the state of the industrial market renders it impossible...to supply impliments for immediate disposal'.

Trade section c.1908

Photo: Margaret Duff Collection

There were, however, displays of marrows, roots and some specimens of potato 'which looked exceedingly fine sent in by Mr J.R. Airey of Patton.' Mr T. Rogers Shaw of Hincaster, Milnthorpe sent a collection of fruit to illustrate the varieties which could be grown in this district which 'drew some favourable comments'. For the ghoulish the Westmorland and Cumberland joint Agricultural Committee had a display of diseases including carrot fly, cabbage fly, white moth, winter moth, magpie moth, American gooseberry mildew, British hawk moth and onion white moth. More positively they showed 'Whitehall, Victory Bishop, Great Scott and Majestic potatoes which are all practically immune from disease'. Fruit again was to the fore in 1922 with displays from the Lyth Valley of Victoria plums and a red Victoria cooking apple. 'Another variety which looked exceptionally well was the Red Bismarck...'. There was now a fruit competition class which attracted a score of entries. Unfortunately Mrs Cottam of Levens 'who had one of the best displays' was disqualified because she did not name the varieties. As regards later horticultural schedules nothing came of a display mounted by the government of Canada also in 1921 of how to grow flax. On the other hand a new age for gardeners was heralded by 'quite a novelty in the district shown by Messrs F.S. Reed and Son...in the form of a self propelled lawn mower, which despite the fact that it is fitted with a two stroke internal combustion engine muttered away in quite an unconcerned manner and kept remarkably cool although the engine is only air cooled'.

Handicrafts on display never came anywhere near to the twee folk weave, carved crook exhibitions of later times though in 1921 St. Dunstan's had 'a small but interesting stand of baskets made by blind soldiers'. Most displays remained excessively practical such as 'the stand occupied by Broomby's of Carnforth which was skilfully laid out, making a special feature of poultry houses ranging in price from 38s 6d to £12'.

Perhaps Broomby's inducement worked for, in the 1930's, poultry sections were added to the show schedules. These, however, never amounted to much. The highest entry number was 85 in 1936 which dropped to 58 in 1938 when all the game bird classes were won by P. Dibble of Ambleside, and D. Medcalf of Endmoor won all 14 (!) classes for Bantams.

Strangely one of the most popular sections of later shows - the Dogs - was lacking for most of the period. After 1902 it was decided to drop the dog section as there were 'too few really working sheep dogs entered'. During the 1920's and 30's a dog show was generally held in Kendal on the same day as the County Show but did not come under the Society's remit. The dog show report was, however, invariably printed alongside that of THE show.

Side shows, minority classes, boozing and entertainment apart the main objects of the Society were displayed in the principal classes. The late nineteenth century pattern of classes persisted until 1938.

'Crops, Turnips and general Stock' were always the first category listed in the Comparative Tables in the *Westmorland Gazette's* report of the show. In the 1920's there were two sections, 'Crops and farms' and 'Roots at Show'; later these were amalgamated as 'Crops and farms'. Although the improvement of agricultural holdings was, perhaps, the cardinal object of the Society this section never seems to have elicited much enthusiasm, perhaps because unlike championship stock the farmer's effort could not be readily admired on a single day. Moreover with so many features to be taken into account such as the state of the weather at judging time entries were always chancy, while the opportunities to criticise the judge's decision along the lines 'he should have seen the crop last week or next week' were proportionately greater. Even in the Centenary Show the entries at 81 were down on the 99 for 1896 and 101 for 1901. Post First World War entries remained reasonably constant with a peak at the 1937 show of 82 entries for crops and farms and 67 for roots. Competition was encouraged by firms selling fertilisers and in 1910 'a monster silver challenge cup awarded by the Potash Syndicate' was won by W.E. Barnes of Ackenthwaite for producing on two acres 11 tons, 14cwt and 2qrs of swedes. Other commercially sponsored awards were for sugar beet from D. Sankey and Co., and for Round Potatoes and Kidney Potatoes by Sutton's seeds who occasionally varied their largesse to include turnips, Long Red Mangolds and Globe Mangolds. With better land the southern area scooped the cultivation prizes. Thus in 1928 the 'best acre of permanent grass' prize went to W. Casson of Beetham, for two acres of mangels to E. Nelson of Lancaster while the prize for a 'crop of mangold wurzels' was won by E. Bainbridge of Holme who also came top for '40 acres in general cultivation'. Later years were no different and in 1937 A. Stables of Holme came first in the best small farm in general cultivation and W. Garnett, junior, got first for best four acres of swedes.

Surprisingly there was relatively little interest in collections of farm stock although the bigger landlords like Lord Henry Bentinck, the Society and the Kendal Corporation all offered awards especially for tenant farmers. When in 1909 the mayor of Kendal handed the Kendal Trades Challenge Cup to Mr Atkinson of Overthwaite he said 'it was very creditable to him, though hardly creditable to the farmers of the district as there were only three competitors', the others being Mr W. Cottam of Low Levens and Mr Airey of Patton.

The emphasis on roots and grass underlines the show's main interest - stock. Always the *Westmorland Gazette* headed its detailed description of the entries with 'Shorthorns' though from 1928 cattle were sub-divided into 'Open' and STF - 'small tenant farmers'. Cattle reports stretched in tiny print down two long columns of the broadsheet about twice as long as the sheep report. The 1899 cattle entries were the best yet being 173 compared to 146, 124, 116 and 83 in the previous four years. Unusually the Centenary Show's record was broken several times with 195 entries in 1907, 185 in 1908, 180 in 1921, 176 in 1922, 209 in 1926 and 191 in 1932. The figures for the later years were, indeed, even better for from 1928 in addition to the open Shorthorn class there were classes for small tenant farmers and in two years Friesians were shown. Though the headline in 1927 ran 'British Friesians make their first appearance' this innovation did not amount to much. Only females were shown and 'there was a good deal of room for improvement' among the 14 beasts entered by two competitors. The first prize went to Mr Wood with a 'weighty beast not yet calved; H.H. Llewellyn lost out in width and depth and third, 'Alao', also Mr Llewellyn's, was too patchy and deep in the bag'. Llewellyn was, however, consoled by prizes for a heiffer not yet in milk with 'Danallan Haslena Gladeye' and 'Culdethal Hettie'. His 'Mansfield Dewdrop' was the 'best bodied beast in the show and would have been higher but for a bad bag'.

In 1928 H.H. Llewellyn was the only exhibitor with ten 'remarkable specimens of this grand bagged type'. But the Friesian day had not yet dawned and there were no more entries until after the Second World War when they swept the board.

The Shorthorn reigned supreme. 'It is nice and cheering' extolled the *Gazette* in 1900 'to be able to say from year to year that the stock exhibited is more numerous and of better quality than ever but this cannot go on for ever'. In that year the prize exhibitors were the Mortons of Skelsmergh Hall, the Handleys of Greenhead with W. Atkinson of Overthwaite following close up. 'The most persevering exhibitors (i.e. most consistently unsuccessful) were the Aireys of Patton'. To stimulate further improvements Mr Bromley-Wilson (later Sir Maurice) of Dallam Tower offered a special prize for cattle from within 15 miles of Kendal where he said, 'there are probably more local shows with a higher class of cattle than anywhere else in the British Isles'. Nevertheless, even at the turn of the century there were indications that the trend for big beef cattle was beginning to wane for greater emphasis was now placed on milking qualities. 'Instruction should be given to judges' ran a new rule in 1899, 'to make milking capacity and form of udder one of the chief points in awarding prizes to pure bred Shorthorn cows and heifers'. By 1903 it was being argued that 'because of dairying Kendal could secure a better show earlier in the year. Westmorland is essentially a dairying county and this point is more important than putting on of flesh'. None of the leading breeders headed by John Handley of Greenhead farm, Hincaster, Milnthorpe would have agreed. Up until 1913 the chief prizes on the field and commercially went to beef cattle especially bulls for export. In 1903 it was noted that 'for some time there has been great demand for the very best specimens for exportation and it is not to be wondered at that agents have been very busy round Kendal and many have gone abroad'. John Handley whose 'Lord James Douglass' won the special Centenary medal for the best male shorthorn in 1899 was reputed to have sold several bulls for several thousands of pounds each - enough to buy outright many a Westmorland farm. He was a principal advisor to the Board of Agriculture and having won the Championship at the Royal and the Royal Windsor/Berkshire had been presented to Queen Victoria. His nephew John Handley of Heversham Hall was also present and was still telling the tale in the 1960's. In 1921 he went out to Argentina to advise on the development of South American beef which in retrospect was as suicidal an action as when contemporaries started up the Japanese motor industry.

Already by the early 1900's John Handley and big beef's greatest days were over. In 1903 no Handley bulls were entered and the best bull was Mr Bateman's 'Duke of Tyne', which had 'good size and a grand underline', followed by bulls belonging to James Woof of Great Strickland and W.G. Atkinson of Raines Hall. 'Many well known names are dropping out and are not being replaced by others equally good' moaned Lord Henry Bentinck in 1904 when the championship went to Mr Graham Ingram's 'Stamp'. He, however, 'was of the very best quality and substance but just a little defective in the legs but bred from one of Mr Handley's bulls'. In this show old John's bull 'San Francisco' came third. There was controversy in 1905 when an outsider Prince Loo, 'a very nice roan', the property of Mr Bainbridge of Greenland's, Carnforth, won the yearling bull class. The general opinion was that one bred by Mr Kendall of Farleton should have won. Even so it was noted that even in the past 'when judges had been local men there was always great jealousy and even now it is occasionally suggested that they know something of some animal or owner which prevents them from being perfectly impartial.' This 'suggestion' might indeed have applied to John Handley - the best known breeder in the land - as he led round the winning Old Bull 'Heather Bloom'. The next year the Handley bull 'Moonstone' was beaten

into second place by Mrs J.C. Topping's 'Pearl King'. With less than strict impartiality the *Gazette* asserted that 'Moonstone' was 'one of the best

Johnny Wilson with his 'red older and bigger bull which will pay for its keep' 1908

ever seen in the Kendal ring...with a splendid back and underline and looks like being a good grower'. Westmorland bulls were well to the fore in 1908 when the prizes for two to six year olds went to W. Atkinson of Overthwaite (who also won the cup for the best kept farm), John Handley and to Lord Brougham and Vaux of Brougham. In reserve was 'a red older and bigger bull which will pay well for its keep' belonging to John Wilson of Crosby Lodge, Ackenthwaite. The champion bull calf belonged to the Richardsons of Laverock Bridge, who went on to have innumerable successes at later shows. Pedigrees continued to decline and in 1910 only four were shown out of an entry of nine for dairy cattle of which the first prize went out of the county to Mr Tom Hunter of Dolphinholme for 'Cherry Star', a 'beautiful shaped red cow with a big but not very pretty bag'. A significant change occurred in 1911 when for the first time dairy cattle were placed at the head of the show description though much attention was still given to the best yearling bull won by R. Burton of Ploughlands. It was also seen that stock breeders 'had learnt their lesson about fat' with the result that yearling bulls were 'about the best ever seen'. The only grumble, in what was regarded as a 'very good show' was that the names of competitors should be given out: 'The committee can have no idea how cross it makes the general public if they can't find out who the animals belong to. Numbers should be larger and more

Prize winning bull calf belonging to W. Richardson, Laverock Bridge c.1908

'Maggie' who weighed 1 ton 14 lbs won the shorthorn 'Stock Cow' class for W. Richardson of Laverock Bridge in 1922 and 1923

prominently displayed'. A more severe criticism was made of dairy cattle in 1912 as bags were too small while 'Mr Tom Hunter of Dolphinholme had a very good cow with a very large bag but it was hopelessly spoiled by the ugly teats'. As regards the entries even big farmers still found it difficult to find three good dairy cows to show together. Beef still held the public's attention and there were cheers for Mr Handley when he was awarded first prize for his yearling bull having conceded the championship in Old Bulls to Mr J.D. Taylor of Crosby Lodge, Shap.

When after a six year gap Westmorland's cattle were judged again, in 1919, everyone bemoaned the absence of the old time breeders like Mr Morton of Skelsmergh who with his 'very old and famous herd is no more'. Mr Handley had only three young bulls entered while Mr Atkinson 'formerly of Overthwaite' and Lord Henry Bentinck had no entries in the dairy classes which were still depressed. Mr Dobson of Holme Park was the only entry in the three cow class but there were some good dairy heifers from Haverflatts, Castlebank and The Howe, Lyth. Quality improved in 1920 with five good bagged cows turned out by Messrs Logan and Kirkby topping the class. 1921 saw the 'finest collection of Shorthorns ever seen in Kendal'. There were nine entries for dairy cows in the milk class in which Mr J. Moffat took first and third and Mr Richardson's 'Wild Rosebud 8th' took second. She had given $27^{1/2}$lbs of milk compared to the winning 'Countess of Fyth's $33^{3/4}$lbs. Even dairymen were confused by the rules introduced for this section which contained such complexities as '5 year old cow calved within two months has to give 30lbs, between two and three calendar months 27lbs, a 4 year old 26lbs and in second month 23lbs; a three year old heiffer 22lbs and 19lbs and a two year old 18lbs and 15lbs.'

There were only four shorthorns in the aged bull class in 1922 which was won by W. Richardson's 'Basing', which had previously won at the Royal Lancashire Show, and beat Mr Handley's thick bodied 'Badminton Rose Briar'. In 1925 the main beef laurels went to Major Penrhyn Hornby of Dalton Hall for his 'Clipper Boy', a 'beautifully modelled red, grand fleshy good bodied sort, level on top and with a good underline and well down on his thighs'. Also in beef Messrs Lewis and sons' 'Dictator' was noted in 1926 as being 'massive, dark roan of tremendous girth, splendid proportions and symmetry'. Full details were also provided (in 1924) of Mrs Dobson's winning two year old heiffer which 'had a good beautifully clinking bag'. Amongst the tenant farmers in the early twenties Mr C. Dobson was the most successful cattle exhibitor with entries which were 'exceedingly praiseworthy'. In 1936 he won '5 championships together with many first prizes'. Close rivals were Mr R. Bindloss of Natland who in 1929 was a popular winner with a 'spangled cow of cross breed' and Mr W. Ward of Lambrigg who won the best cow for dairy purposes in 1931. In the same year a return to old times was indicated when Lord Henry Bentinck's 'Underley Pansy' won the best bull calf class. The Small Tenants winner was M.R. Mawson with 'Orton Supreme'. In 1932 many of the top prizes went out of the county and Mr J. Barnes of Wigton, Cumberland had a good winner with an 'outstanding heiffer 'Dupplin Winsonia''. Other good entries were a fine bull belonging to H. Woof of Burton and a 'grand cow in calf with a beautiful vessel' owned by Mr C.E. Bateman. The big surprise of the day was a natural one when the second prize winner of the cow in calf class belonging to a Ravenstonedale farmer gave

birth to a calf on the field. This happy event was described as 'a very rare occurrence'.

Descriptions of winning beasts remained colourful. J. Moffat's best recorded cow in milk

Walter Thexton and daughter Madge with prize shorthorn c.1930

in 1935 was 'of strong character, clean fleshed and good in touch but just a shade strong in the hocks'. At the same show H. Mather of Staveley had in 'Calcaria Marksman', the Royal Lancashire champion, 'a bull of wonderful dual character, deep bodied, straight, good underlined and good in its movements'. In 1936 G.R.H. Smith produced a winner at Lanes Farm, Preston Richard [later the site of the County Show], 'Barrington Ward', a wealthy type of Shorthorn character, 'good ueshed (sic) and most neatly moulded though a little heavy in bone'. At the Coronation Show of 1937 dairying was prominent when the winners for best cows in milk classes were R.L. Raby of Morecambe and second W.H. Nelson 'with grand bagged cows'. The final post first world war - or pre second war - show had an old fashioned flavour when much was made of the winner in the beef class of a 'two year old and upwards' bull belonging to H.B. Allison of Penrith which was 'a grand sire of the real Scotch Shorthorn type and shown in the pink of condition and wrapped in a wonderful hide'. Mr Allison also won with a yearling bull which, 'if possible, was in even better mould'.

Sheep classes always attracted the most entries but numbers fluctuated from year to year. The record of 316 entries for the 1899 show was never again approached let alone equalled but other good years were 256 in 1904, 220 in 1910, 232 in 1922 and 275 in 1925. Bad years were 140 entries in 1919, 121 in 1931, 119 in 1934 and 137 in 1938. Classification was equally inconsistent. Sometimes Westmorland's 'own' breed the Herdwicks were in and sometimes they were deleted as were Swaledales, while Suffolks were variously judged with Downs and sometimes separately. Generally there were classes for Suffolks, Wensleydales or Blue Faced, Rough Fell or Kendal Roughs, Longwoolled and

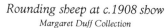

Rounding sheep at c.1908 show
Margaret Duff Collection

Champion Herdwick ram 1910

Half Bred sheep. Constant swapping and changing must have been very confusing for entrants and for judges. In 1899 the *Gazette* magnanimously remarked that the 'Scotch blackfaced sheep were judged by a Yorkshireman but they met with fair treatment notwithstanding, except that in one or two cases the places might have been a little different'. The following year it was again held "t judge est git it wrang agin' especially in Shropshires. Although there were only four competitors for Longwools - 'won by Moss End' - 'the placings in the class for ewes and gimmer lambs might have been reversed with advantage'. In particular Messrs Gibsons' 'undoubtedly' should have beaten Mr R.J. Huddleston's sheep which had, in any case, won five first places. Mr Huddlestone had, the reporter added - apparently reproachfully, 'spent a lot of money on high priced tups'. Greater credit was given to the Underley flock master who won the Wensleydale Blue Faced Sheep Breeders prize and also to the Rough Fell sheep from the Grayrigg and Selside district belonging to Messrs E. Swidebank, J. Shuttleworth, H. Wharton and J. Wood. Scotch Black Faces, 'one of the best mountain sheep', were seen to be an up and coming breed. Longwoolled sheep classes were dominated by a few breeders throughout the period notably the Dargues of Burneside Hall and the Woods of Cooper House, Selside. There was early controversy in 1900 when a class for 'Longwool not qualified to compete as Wensleydales' was introduced. This class was won by the executors of

'Lucky Jim' (left) champion Wensleydale

J. Dargue but the 'palm' for 'about the best sheep shown at Kendal' was awarded to Mr J. Dobson of Burton. A predicted winner failed to materialise, however, as a shearing ram belonging to Lord Henry Bentinck met with an accident before the show and so only managed a third. The winner was Mr H.L. Storey who 'swept the board with nice classy shearlings with good broad backs and well sprung ribs'. In the 'good' year 1904 extra prizes like a thirty shilling barometer donated by Mr Heap the chemist for nine tup lambs increased interest. In the next year or two the most creditable entries came mainly from the southern part of the district with John Dobson of Burton winning the aged ram class, Mr R. Parker of Moss End taking all nine prizes in the shearling Shropshire ram classes well ahead of entries from the estates of Mr Storey of Lancaster and Mr Victor Cavendish of Holker. In 1907, an otherwise disappointing year with many 'limited breeds' was redeemed by a 'rare exhibition' of Wensleydales shown by Lord Henry Bentinck, a grand Black Faced ram with a magnificent fleece from Mr T. Irving's flock at Forest Hall and 'gradely' Longwoolled 'uns' put in by Rowland Parker who won three classes in which a lady, Mrs Turner of Murley Moss, came a 'worthy second'. The only surprise was that the Rough Fell Ram belonging to Joseph Wood of Cooper House was beaten by Mr C. Airey's ram which was eight years old.

There was some dropping off in Shropshires and Herdwicks in the immediate pre First World War period which was balanced by an increase in Longwoolled sheep including Lincolns and Border Leicesters. The leading breeders invariably were Dobsons of Burton who won five out of six classes in 1912 and Lord Henry Bentinck whose Wensleydale Shearling Ram 'Royal Bertie's Hero' had beaten 'every thing every where this season'. In the immediate post First World War period Black Faced and Wensleydales retained their popularity but Rough Fells were again to the fore with good displays particularly in 1921 when J. Hudson's ancient ram and J. Wood's tup lambs were of 'Royal Show quality'. Though 'rather out of the Herdwick district it is nevertheless surprising', the *Gazette* commented, 'what an excellent collection of the hardy little mountain sheep

Joseph Wood of Cooper House with his champion Rough Fell ram and ewe 1908

find their way year by year to Kendal'. For a change the winners came from the Lake District proper being Messrs Gregg of Troutbeck and Messrs Atkinson of Sawrey. Half bred lambs with plenty of Rough Fells, Leicesters and Black Faced came in quantity in the next years but Wensleydales from Lord Henry Bentinck were absent in 1923 though other flockmasters had plenty of entries. Longwoolled prizes were scooped by Mrs Edmonson of New Hutton in 1925 except for the aged ram which was won by W.J. Postlethwaite's entry being 'a grand topped, good fleshed sheep, like getting a fat lamb'. Leicester sheep were up in 1926 perhaps encouraged by a new silver challenge tankard which was won initially by Mr Dobson for 'a well bred sure footed animal with a neat coat'. Lakeland was again successful in the early 1930's with fell sheep. In 1930 J. Hudson was a popular winner with a Rough Fell aged ram beating Sir Samuel Scott's 'which has always topped the class'. This time it came second just ahead of 'a very useful animal' belonging to J.D.C. Wharton of Mart Close, Kendal. 1931, a down year, saw a 'wonderful achievement' by J. Dargue who won the championship for male and female crossbreeds. Surprisingly the Longwoolled championship was carried off by Messrs Phizacklea of Ulverston. Westmorland was again more successful in the next years. Mr Armistead of Grayrigg after eight successive victories won the cup outright in 1933 for Shearlings as well as having a champion shearling lamb which was 'well nigh perfect having won everywhere else'. Indeed, despite a fall in entries at the show all seemed well with local sheep especially from the fells. The work of promoters like Sir Samuel Scott seemed to have borne fruit when Sir Samuel himself was beaten for his own challenge cup for a Rough Fell ram by Mr T. Nicholson of Cookson Tenement, Howgill.

From start to last in the period the highest prominence was given to the horses - heavy/agricultural and light/hunters. Although in 1938 there were only 53 heavy horses entered compared to 160 in 1898 the *Gazette*, nevertheless, gave pride of place to the photograph of them parading against an ironic background of parked ringside motor vehicles. There were a near incredible 242 entries for Light horses in 1899 almost implying that well mounted and drawn show patrons simply entered the animals which would be taking them to the show anyway. The figure is all the more remarkable as Westmorland was not a 'mounted hunting' county and so almost all hunters entered came from away, often as far afield as Yorkshire and Derbyshire. Hunters and Ladies hacks were not numerous in 1900 when there was 'nothing special' in light horses except for 'Princess' from the Dallam Tower stable. Heavy horses were divided into two classes for Clydesdales and Shires but there were 'few entries' (in fact 110) and the overall winner was Mr Dowbiggin's 'Scottish Mysor'. In 1901 there were good Clydesdale fillies - 'good featured, nicely marked and strong bodied' - from Mr Lowis' farm at Temple Sowerby but quality was much better the following year when out of eleven Clydesdale mares there was 'not a bad one in the lot of them'. In light horse Victor Cavendish's brown mare 'Festive' triumphed over Mr Fox's black mare 'Helvedon' and Mr Whittaker's shapely 'Missing Link'. The best exhibition ever, better than the centenary, was the verdict in 1903 when the

Light Horse champion was a chestnut mare 'Lady Waterbury' belonging to Moses Robinson who had bought her for only 25gns at Crewe. So important were heavy horses that there were two parade rings from 1903 when the victrix was Mr E. Whitwell's roomy grey mare which 'has had a most successful season and wound it up by annexing the green card' though she had a strong rival in Mr Victor Cavendish's bay eight year old 'Borough'. A more democratic or patronising gesture was made in 1904 with the introduction of a class 'for a turnout of the property of a tenant farmer; the good upkeep of the conveyance and harness to be taken into account - not its newness - and that it should be driven by a farmer's wife or daughter who takes produce to Kendal Market.' Although this attracted entries from around the county the most frequent winners of this class were the wife and daughters of John Wilson of Ackenthwaite. Such encouragement also led to an improvement in Cobs and Ponies who put on a 'smart array' in 1905. The keenest interest at the next show centred on hunters where there was rivalry between the ultimate winner, a fine old mare 'Ting a ling' belonging to Mr J.S. Rigg, and a three year old gelding 'Masterpiece' belonging to Dr E.S. Jackson of Carnforth which had swept all before it at other shows that season and 'obtained the Hunter's Improvement Society's Challenge Cup and Imperial Stud Book Society's Medal'.

Heavy horses were 'pleasing and disappointing' in 1907. Set against the previous years the Shire champions 'Holywell Spot' and 'Holker Princess' (which won again for Victor Cavendish) Clydesdales had 'gone off' and entries were down. Quality picked up in 1908 when Mr Dawson Green's 'Primrose' won the Shire horse championship having 'great substance, great depth of rib, plenty of bone, sound feet and moves freely'. The light horses were 'amongst the best ever seen' (a recurring accolade!) and, in particular, Mr Fred Armstrong's 'Emma' stood out 'with all the grace of a hunter mare with plenty of room'.

It was in 1908 that Messrs J. and G. Dickinson of Cark Mills really established themselves as the leading light horse contenders at Kendal, a position they held until the Second World War. For their virtual debut a three year old brown gelding 'Cark Majesty' was acclaimed as 'being big with clean active movements, which will make him a really classy hunter - one likely to stand a long and stern chase across open country'. In the next years more thoroughbred sires for cross breed dual purpose horses were required and for their progeny a new class was introduced - disastrously. In 1910 though there was prize money amounting to £27 6s on the table most of the cross entries were 'really hunters' putting the judge Mr Hutchinson in a quandary which he at length resolved by disqualifying 13 out of 15 entries. The winner belonged to the Misses Tugman of Winster and was 'strong and cobby but could do with a little more size'. Just before the First World War Clydesdales were still down and there were only five entered in 1912 compared to 13 Shires though there were some good entries from Messrs T.H.

Heavy horses well to the fore at the 1908 show
Margaret Duff Collection

Croasedale and J. Farrer from Furness. Clydesdales were, however, in big demand as 'Canadian farmers have been advertising for mares of quality'. One such quality horse was certainly 'Jesse' who won for Mr Irving of Newby in 1911. Light horse classes were still heavily contested and judging could be a lengthy affair. In 1913 the two main contenders in three year olds were tried over and over again before the judge pronounced that Messrs Howarth's chestnut filly was a better horse than Mr Hully's chestnut gelding.

Good entries in the immediate post war period for heavy horses confirmed the impression that the general motorisation of the countryside was still some time off. Indeed the show catalogues hardly hint that the internal combustion engine had been invented. In 1925 the Provincial Insurance Company advertised full cover 'at a low rate' for a Morris motor car but it was not until 1932 that tractor oil was advertised and the first advert for a Fordson tractor appeared in 1932. A decline in heavy horses was attributed not to tractors but to 'the matter of shoeing which are required before the horses are allowed to enter the ring'. The responsibility for a 'falling off' in light horses was more obvious 'but what can be expected when the hum of the motor car has superseded the jingle of traces on our mountain passes and...when Westmorland enjoys the distinction of having almost more cars per population than any district in the world and when the county is supplied with one of the best bus services in the country'. It was, therefore, a matter of congratulation that there were 9 heavy horses (won by Cornthwaites of Milnthorpe) in 1921, and lovely clean limbed hunters like H.L. Storey's 'Boathouse' which won for several years on the trot. Other local breeders like Miles Mason of Crosthwaite who won with a three year old filly in 1929 also did well at this time. None, however, could beat the Dickinsons who led with 'Cark Bridgett' in 1926 and a 2,000 guinea 'Sea Breeze' in 1930. 'Sea Breeze' was then only four and competing every year she saw out the period

Fell ponies

gaining a second place as a twelve year old in the 1938 show when she was beaten by 'Sunshine' belonging to Mr Dobson of Sampool, Levens. Fell ponies were introduced at the 1926 show and then, and for succeeding shows, Mr De Vere Irving was the leading entrant. When his fell pony 'Stonecross Daisy' won in 1932 the *Gazette* said that she with other equestrian entries 'represented the best talent not only in the County but in the whole of England in the light horse class'. Outstanding competitors were E. Johnson's 'Grasscutter' and T. Main of Castleford's 'Hunger' who won the hunter capable of carrying 15 stone in 1932. Children were now being encouraged and competitors came from near and far. The winner in 1932 for a Pony not more than 14 hands high and ridden by a child came from Blundell Sands Riding School, Merseyside, in 1932.

One slight sign of changing times was that it was no longer essential to have two rings for judging heavy horses which were now paraded in the main ring in front of the grandstands. Entries by 1930 were below 50 but much was made of the leading agricultural horses which included Mr J.R. Winter's 'Tommy' and 'Jack' best pair of matched plough horses in 1932, 'Endmoor Iron Cladia', a three year old shire belonging to J.R. Tomlinson in 1935 and 'Ancliff Future Queen' which belonged to William Newhouse of Slyne and which won for five consecutive years. Setting a pattern for later times women were already becoming officially prominent in the horse classes. There were several women patrons who offered prizes for instance for the development of ladies hacks as a class while Miss Ethel Lees of Burton Hall won several times with brood mares or brood mares with foal in the agricultural classes. 'Twin Ladies judge Clydesdales' was the byline to the show report of 1937. It referred to 'the Misses Park of Portobello, two attractive and intelligent Scottish lassies who handled the feet and limbs of the stallions with an assurance which would have done credit to a Gretna Green blacksmith'. They awarded the top prizes to Mr Armstrong of Staveley's mare while the winning pair of shires belonged, once again, to Mr Newhouse of Slyne.

Second only to the Shorthorns the longest reports of the show were for what were called, in the days long before 'political correctness', the 'women's sections'. At first their classes were listed under 'butter' although the awards were categorised in their husbands' or the farms' names. 'Butter' from time to time was stretched to include cheese, cream cheese, eggs, dressed poultry, a surprisingly small amount of baking and handicrafts. From 1923 when it was reported that almost every WI branch in the county was represented the dairying displays were shown alongside competitions staged by the Westmorland Federation of Women's Institutes whose contribution to the show, as in rural life generally was, possibly, the most positive social development of the period.

Great ladies of the Edwardian period including Queen Alexandra, who had an elaborate dairy constructed for her own use at Sandringham, vied with each other in championing the dairy maid's art. Westmorland's dairy queens from the 1900's into the 1920's and 1930's remained Countess Bective and her daughter Lady Henry Bentinck of Underley. In 1902 there were 183 butter entries: 'As soon as the entrance was raised there was the customary inrush of farmers dames and daughters eager to view the distribution of prizes by Lady Henry Bentinck'. Other lady supporters were Lady Bagot of Levens, Mrs Crewdson of Helme Lodge and Mrs Jacob Wakefield of Sedgwick House. The latter ladies were particularly useful as they allowed their dairies to be used for the storage of butter which had to be entered ten days before show day in order to test its keeping quality. In 1914 the 'keeping time' was extended to twenty days. For some reason Mrs Crewdson's name and others were 'struck out from the catalogue' in1903 and entries dropped although the quality was considered to be 'a great advance' on the Centenary Show. One reason was that the Cumberland and Westmorland farm school at Newton Rigg had started a travelling dairy course which sent tutors to different districts instructing young women in the latest techniques. Residential courses were also available but these did not catch on noticeably for girl students until the 1920's. In 1908 there were 22 exhibitors for Lady Henry Bentinck's prize for butter made under the rules of the school. Before presenting the prizes the judge Mr W.T. Lawrence made some 'instructive' remarks: 'The test was keeping quality...in the case of one of the winning

'Best Butter Ladies'. Winners of the Bentinck prizes c.1914

samples the butter was spongy, but it was the best in flavour, and though its consistency was open to question it came second. In nine out of ten samples sent to market in the ordinary way the loss of flavour was due to the cream being a little tainted. Cream should be scalded where cream was kept for a week before butter making days'. Three years later Mr Lawrence was 'happy' to report that only four out of 23 entries had 'seriously gone off' but he continued 'it always seemed strange to him to get so large a proportion of good butter at the show while only getting a small proportion in the market'. There was still a good deal to be learned including how cream could get 'germs of mould'. For good measure he added that no one knew what cream cheese was although he agreed (would he have dared to disagree?) with Captain Bagot MP that 'it should be absolutely sweet like solid cream'. The butter presentation provided the main speech making opportunity of the day. In 1913 it was reported that the Mayor 'spoke briefly' but the synopsis of his worship's remarks filled two thirds of a column of tiny print. He 'congratulated them all on a good haytime and harvest for they all liked to see progress but at the same time they must not pat themselves on the back or shake hands with themselves too freely.' It was no doubt after such treats of municipal eloquence that Sir John Weston introduced the 'strictly two minute speech'. Lt Col Fothergill, the President in 1922, perhaps broke the brevity rule as he expounded on 'the fact that the butter of Westmorland thirty years ago was extremely bad; but now it is quite good due to Newton Rigg. Everything he saw was up to standard except in fruit'. Almost all fruit entries came from the milder Arnside, Lyth and Kendal areas as a late frost had destroyed the blossom elsewhere in the county.

By the late twenties domestic section classes had expanded, the most popular being four classes of butter for Lady Henry Bentinck's, Lady Bagot's, Society's Special and Major Hoggarth's prizes; cream cheese, dressed poultry or fowl for market; home baked white bread; brown bread from Beacon Flour Company; six oat cakes; honey 4lbs; hen eggs white and brown; duck eggs white and tinted; desert and 'cooker' apples; pears and damsons. In 1930 when because the tent had blown down there were few prize winners present at the makeshift show in the Auction Mart there were still 'meritorious tables of butter, bread, eggs and cheese which indicated that despite wireless, pictures, motors and labour problems the women on our Westmorland farms were every bit as efficient as their menfolk'. Moreover one WI member Mrs Finch Dawson who was at the top of the prize list in the 'butter' tent had also 'gained the winning ticket for the best Shorthorn heiffer'. Contrary to some memories disputes over the tents between the show committee and WI executive did not lead to a fall off in WI involvement and in 1931 there were 343 Institute entries ranging in popularity from 41 entries for bottled fruit down to 6 for cream cheese and three for syrup. 'Handicrafts made during the year' included baskets, chair caning,

Farming was still a family affair - Auntie Tyson (on churn) and family.
Haytime at Preston Patrick 1939
Margaret Duff Collection

crochet, dyeing, furcraft, gloving, leather work, raffia rugs, rush work, plain sewing, smocking, slippers, spinning, string seated stools, soft and hard toys, quilting and weaving. There were also demonstrations of bottling fruit by Newton Rigg, chair caning by Mrs Barge of Kearstwick Institute and in upholstery by Miss Bonney of Staveley. Congratulating the creators of the crafty cornucopia Lady Maureen Stanley, wife of the MP for Westmorland, enthused 'if the worst comes to the worst and as you know we are in the midst of a financial crisis (Britain had just left the Gold Standard) obviously Westmorland is going to be the place to live in. Judging from the excellence of the exhibits of bread if we stay in our homes we will not starve'. These remarks were followed by 'laughter' which was also the response in 1932 when 'after Lady Henry Bentinck gave out her prizes it was discovered that they had been confused with the special prizes given by Lady Bagot. Fortunately nine of the prize winners had not left the tent and the occurrence was cheerfully passed off'.

Fortunately too Westmorland and England, in the wider sphere, passed through the slump of the early thirties and the happier tenor of the times was reflected in 'bumper crowds' at the show. Though a Bad Season had affected entries gate receipts were up by £105 in 1938 when a 'record attendance' provided the Society with an 'encouraging 140th birthday present'. But while Westmorland folk were revelling in the display of their success in fusing old and new on the land outside, in the wider world, 'post-war' had stealthily made way for 'pre-war'. At the right hand column of the *Westmorland Gazette's* full page report of the show on the 17th September 1938 there was an announcement in bold type: 'Mr Chamberlain Returning' but after 'consulting the cabinet he will meet Herr Hitler again in the next few days'. The British Prime Minister's object was to avert war but as the whole world has never ceased to forget - or forgive - his return to Munich did not bring 'peace in our time' and eleven months later this country was, consequently, at war with Germany. Only a brief statement was necessary the next September to inform Westmerians that, though the event was only a fortnight off and 'everything was prepared' there would be no show in 1939 - nor would there be for the duration. Farming folk as in 1799 and 1914 once more had to bend themselves to 'furnishing tables in the presence of our foes'. But while the world bled it was to be boom time for British agriculture.

CHAPTER FIVE

The Second Agricultural Revolution
1940-1999

Britain's second Agricultural Revolution was stimulated by the Second World War. Westmorland being far away from any battle or blitz zones was officially a 'safe area' and was, indeed, arguably one of the safest regions in the world at war. Even so a thousand service men and a few Westmorland service women laid down their lives including the Agricultural Society's secretary Michael Hodgson. As tragic and much more strange was the slaughter 'by enemy action' of the Wood family of Selside, one of Westmorland's leading yeoman dynasties and the frequent winners, in pre-war days, of the fell sheep championships, who died in 1942 when their farm Cooper House was hit by jettisoned bombs. But for most Westmerians the main impact of what sixty years later was still called 'The War' was social and economic. Town and country came together instantly in the autumn of 1939 with the arrival of evacuees while later on Land Girls, from the Women's Land Army, and Italian and German

Above: The Friesian future.
Calves standing on what is now the route of the M6 at Crooklands Photo: H.G.Clark

123

Prisoners of War were 'brought in' to provide crucial agricultural labour. As between 1914 and 1918, the impetus was on arable cultivation for grain and potatoes. But this time the demands of what was regarded as 'a balanced diet' required dairy products, especially milk which was provided free or cheaply in hitherto undreamed of amounts to school children, young mothers and invalids. To ensure supply the government through the Milk Marketing Board guaranteed prices and sales and the certainty of the monthly 'milk cheque' was, for the next forty years, probably the single greatest economic incentive to the modernisation of local agriculture. Similar subsidies and guarantees were made for other stock and crops while the snoopings of officials from the County War Agricultural Committee ensured that Ministry diktats were obeyed. For even the most died in the wool traditionalist there were only two options: 'modernise and make money' or 'get off the land'. Those who stayed on the land and who modernised and expanded prospered as never before so that many tenants were able to become owner occupiers when the great estates, depleted by death duties, were sold up. On the farms two major types of innovation were made to meet the demands of war time and in order to pay off the bank loans on the farm. One was zoological for now, after a century, the monopoly of the Dairy Shorthorns was broken by Friesian cattle. Once dismissed on their brief appearance at the inter-war shows as being 'mere whitewash machines' they came eventually to dominate the Westmorland meadows though it was not until 1960 that there were fewer Shorthorns than Friesians at the show.

The other great change was mechanical. Hands required by the plough meant fewer fingers for the udder and so milking stools made way for milking machines while out on the land the noble Shires and Clydesdales were replaced 'under War Ag.' by Ferguson and Fordson tractors. With a steady phud, phud, phud coming twice daily from the shippon, the clank of aluminium churns being set out on the milk stands by the roadside to await the milk lorry and the regular alternate rumble and roar of the tractors coming in and out of the yard the whole tenor and tempo of rural life changed. Despite the blackout life even became lighter for electric milking machines were easier and more economical than the 'Lister' engines powered by hard to come by petrol and so even in the midst of war the electrification of the countryside, barely begun in 1939, was stepped up. Electric light and appliances along with other labour saving devices such as the Aga cooker with its 'constant hot water' reached the farmhouse as part of a concurrent domestic revolution and helped stimulate the liberation of the farmer's wife. Thanks once more to the Milk Marketing Board and, in South Westmorland, to Libby's Milk canning factory at Milnthorpe, the farmer's wife was now more or less freed from the thraldom of butter and cheese making as most milk now left the farm as liquid.

Households were still large and even after the land girls and POW's had left

NATIONAL SERVICE ᵂ/₃₃

10,000 Women Wanted For Farm Work

A FREE OUTFIT, high boots, breeches, overall and hat.

MAINTENANCE during training.

TRAVELLING expenses in connection with the work.

WAGES 18/- per week, or the district rate, whichever is the higher.

MAINTENANCE during terms of unemployment up to four weeks.

HOUSING personally inspected and approved by the Women's War Agricultural Committee in each County.

WORK on carefully selected farms.

PROMOTION. good work rewarded by promotion and higher pay.

AFTER THE WAR, special facilities for settlement at home or overseas.

DON·T DELAY ENROL TO-DAY

Application forms may be had at all Post Offices & Employment Exchanges.

DIRECTOR GENERAL OF NATIONAL SERVICE.
ST. ERMINS, S.W. 1.

a South Westmorland mixed farm of 100 to 150 acres might employ three or four 'live in' men plus a family of several children and often a grandparent or auntie as well. Five or six meals or snacks consisting of breakfast before and after morning milking, mid morning 'drinking', dinner at noon, tea before and after evening milking and a substantial supper, especially at lambing, haytime, harvest and threshing were still the rule of the day. Not surprisingly there was still neither time nor inclination for the social niceties of the suburbs. It was only in the 1970's that the customs of drinking pre-milking coffee from the porridge bowl and of eating pudding off the same plate as the main course finally disappeared. About the same time the mealtime segregation of the farmer's family eating at the round table in the corner of the kitchen with 'the men an t' girls' sitting on forms at the long table also went out as by the seventies most farm labour was provided by the family. Any hired help lived out and extra seasonal work such as ploughing, hedging and the like were now done by 'agricultural contractors' who drove to work like everyone else. Whatever the safety regulations might say children born

Milking for victory

Victory Churn Contest
(1943 - 44)

This Diploma

is awarded to the Farmer & Farmworkers of

in the county of
in recognition of their loyal work for their Country in its time of need.
The milk production of this Farm showed an increase during the winter period of not less than 10 per cent over the previous year.

on the land after 1939 were likely to have had a steering wheel in their hands at as early an age as their grandparents had first held reins or plough leads. Motoring mobility along with somewhat less irksome work with slightly shorter hours meant that not only the farmer but his wife and children had a little more time to spend off the farm.

More leisure time contributed to the success of the two most successful rural organisations the Women's Institute and the Young Farmers Clubs. Although they had originated before 1939 they blossomed in the post-war world to enhance immensely the quality of rural life. There was certainly room for improvement. Despite later nostalgia what most farmers' wives slammed down on the kitchen table in the 1940's was as utterly unlike 'the Traditional Farm House Fayre', beloved of the Tourist Board, as the bread and scrape in the worker's 'bagging' was a far cry from a pub's 'Ploughman's Lunch'. In the days when she was 'for ever scratting' between kitchen, yard, wash house, dairy and 'doing the rooms' women on the farm could not at the same time be devoting themselves to confectionery, tapestry work or flower arranging. But from the 1940's onwards women threw themselves into competing in the 'domestic' classes with as much zest as their menfolk did in the stock classes. Moreover when it came to horses, dogs, goats, Jersey cattle and Jacob sheep lady entrants invariably outnumbered the men.

Thanks to the YFC's activities, ranging from husbandry (in both senses) to educational visits at home and abroad and public speaking competitions, the music hall stereotype of gormless, mono-syllabic rural youth who knew of 'nowt beyond the next midden' was eradicated. Both the WI's and YFC's used their day out in Kendal (and later Crooklands) on the second Thursday in September as their 'shop window'. Hence as in earlier eras the shows in the half century following the Second World War reflected changes in the way of life of farming folk as much they did innovations in agricultural practice.

The first post-war show, in 1946, was very much an austerity affair. Food rationing meant that there was no catering at all on the field and although a luncheon tent for officials and refreshments for the general public were available in succeeding years there was no return to the sumptuous banquets for 'the county set', nor for the speechifying afterwards. Nevertheless a semblance of former hierarchical times was provided by the presence as Show President of the High Sheriff Mr J.H. Somervell (of K Shoes) who was accompanied by Sir Samuel Scott (of the Provincial Insurance company) and other local dignitaries. Though 'J.H. and Sir Samuel represented modern urban capitalism the survivors of the old landed ruling class remained surprisingly popular perhaps because they no longer did much ruling. Less prominence than in former times was given in the show reports to naming the elite who graced the President's tent. Even so the 1958 account reported the presence of Mr R.A. Somervell, President and

High Sheriff, W.F. Vane MP and Mrs Vane, Lord Lonsdale, the Mayor and Mayoress of Kendal Mr and Mrs R.L. Sheaf, the Mayor and Mayoress of Appleby Mr and Mrs A.E.P. Slack, the Lord Lieutenant Henry Hornyold-Strickland of Sizergh Castle and the Hon Mrs Hornyold-Strickland, P.F. Scott, Chairman, J.W. Barge, Treasurer, J.P. Johnston, assistant treasurer, A.S. Thompson Secretary, W.P. Dobson chairman of the General Committee and J.A. Wood of Helsington, Vice-Chairman. Moreover, most of the High Sheriffs had landed interests with many of them, indeed, coming from the 'oldest' families and so their dual role as Show President continued to seem appropriate. Thus Robin Bagot of Levens Hall was President in 1951 and Captain Michael Stanley of Witherslack in 1959 and Captain Nigel Pease of Underley in 1967 and C.H.D. Acland in 1968. As in pre-war days many other presidents also sported honorary service titles including Brigadier-General L.J. Wyatt in 1948, Captain R.R. Hewetson, 1949, Surgeon Commander W.G. Thwaytes R.N.(retd) 1956, and Colonel J.R. Danson in 1961, while Major T.W. Hedley of Briary Close, Windermere served as both Chairman of the committee and Show President in

Chairman, president and past president at the 1973 show.
L to R: Mr Harold Robinson, Mrs Robinson, Mrs Hedley, Major Hedley,
Mrs Hornyold-Strickland (president), Mr Hornyold-Strickland
Photo: Westmorland Gazette

1965. But times were changing and by the 1960's it was felt that the show did not need the extra cache of having gentry or half gentry to preside over its activities. Moreover the tradition received a long remembered insult and financial blow when one High Sheriff/President sent the treasurer a bill for wine he had served to the show committee while enter-

Mrs Olive Clarke first woman president presents 'Tucker' Mason with the championship cup for Blonde d'Aquitaine 1987 Photo: Westmorland Gazette

taining them in his own mansion. Fortunately an opportunity to depart from tradition occurred when the office of High Sheriff for Westmorland was abolished with the County in 1974. Happily the last High Sheriff/President James Cropper subsequently served as President on two more occasions. From 1974 the custom arose of 'honouring long serving supporters of the Show' by making them President interspersed with the occasional national figure. Thus Mr and Mrs Edwin Ellis did the honours in 1974 when their son Brian was also chairman, Jim Rutter a leading horse man, in 1981, the show's first historian

John Fishwick

Stephen Barratt in 1982 and John Fishwick, for over fifty years the auctioneer at Kendal Auction mart, in 1993. Holding the office actually provided a new opportunity for many of the 'farmer presidents'. George Robinson and his wife Taggie said their presidential show in 1982 was the first time that they had been able to look round 'as normally they were too busy'. 1982 was a good year for the 'Moss End' Robinsons as they had to present themselves with The William Proctor Cup for the best general stock. Equally pleased to do the rounds for the first time was Mr William Robinson of New Hutton who in 1989 looked round the WI tent for the first time but he intended 'to go again next year'.

Show Officers 1978
(Left front row) Mr J. Procter (president-elect), Mr E. N. Croft (president),
Mr E. Ellis (retiring president); (back row) Mr T. Atkinson (vice-chairman),
Mr B Ellis (chairman), Mr R. Morgan (treasurer), Mr Chris Lambert (secretary)
Photo: Westmorland Gazette

When Olive Clarke the doyenne of the WI, agriculture and of almost every aspect of public life became the first lady to hold the office in 1986 she declared 'I can think of few greater honours that can come the way of anyone than to be invited to be president of one of the finest shows in the country'. Such a sentiment was as surely held by her successors who as a lasting honour became life members of the society. Apart from Olive these included in 1999 Major T.W.I. Hedley, MBE, G.E. Robinson, W.A. Atkinson, J.A. Cropper, Rev J. Johnston, W.H. Robinson, Mrs D. Lambert (President elect for 1999), Brian Ellis, John Fishwick, J.V. Gregg and T.D. Edmondson. Although the feeling that 'we don't want champagne and canapés for the select few' remained strong there was also something of a return to more lavish hospitality. The approach of the Bi-centenary led to plans for a special celebration on the 200th birthday itself 24 August 1999 at which the guest of honour would be Lord Plumb, an ecumenical thanksgiving service to be conducted on the Show Field by the Bishop of Carlisle on the Sunday before the show and also hopes that the show day itself might be graced by the presence of a Royal Personage. It was even being whispered that it was about time that the name of the show should be changed to 'The Royal Westmorland' - but the results of such aspirations will belong to a later chapter of the show's history.

Compared to earlier days the post-war shows were rarely used by politicians local or national to make major pronouncements on agriculture or other public issues. There were, however, grumbles made to the Minister of Agriculture (and Westmorland's MP) Michael Jopling about the imposition of European milk quotas in 1984, about the burning by French farmers of British lambs in the early 1990's and about the 'ban on beef' in schools during the BSE scare in 1997. Bravely bearding the Westmorland farming mafia in their den Tony Baldry, Conservative Minister of State at the Ministry of Agriculture, Fisheries

Chris Lambert

and Food diplomatically pronounced that 'it was clearly an excellent show' in 1995. Three years and a 'New' Labour government later the Food Safety minister Jeff Rooker announced in the show's 'great food hall' that 'I will say that British regional foods are better than regional speciality foods abroad - and that is illegal to say under the European Commission'! In that year the President was the former MP Michael Jopling, by now Lord Jopling of Ainderby, who was just beginning to be forgiven for the milk quotas imposed fifteen years earlier. Having visited every show since he became a Prospective Parliamentary Candidate for Westmorland in 1963 the compliments Michael expressed were based on experience but his greatest tributes were reserved for Chris Lambert the recently deceased secretary who had been the lynch pin of the Society for twenty-six years. 'We should all rejoice in this wonderful creation of his and remember what he did for the Westmorland County Show'.

Chris Lambert was not only the longest serving secretary of the twentieth century but one of its most successful organisers. During his first ten years the cattle entries rose from 175 to 321 in 1981, sheep from 320 to 366 and horses from 187 to 378 and numbers increased again in the next ten years. Chris's predecessors had been equally assiduous in sometimes leaner times. Arthur Whitwell was first post-war secretary appointed at a salary of £70 in 1946 when the *Gazette* acknowledged that he with the help of his wife had 'carried out his duties in an efficient manner'. He also set the pattern for a hands on approach to show day as in 1947 he and his staff 'were on duty at 7.30 and by the time the judging started at 10am the spacious showfield was a hive of activity'. In 1949 Alan S. Thompson, already an established Kendal auctioneer, became secretary though he was aided at his first show by Mr and Mrs Whitwell and the officials who now included Mr W. Jordan as Assistant Treasurer who succeeded Sir Samuel Scott as Treasurer the next year with J.W. Barge as his assistant. Under

Alan Thompson, secretary for the next fifteen years, and John Williams of Kentmere, Brian Dakin of Kendal and R.W. Sykes, his successors from 1967 to 72, the show's administration ran smoothly. Moreover after he ceased to be secretary Robert Sykes did good work as the Society's solicitor. Nevertheless by the 1970's it was clear that part time and poorly remunerated staff, however hardworking and experienced, simply could not have the time to organise the major attractions and increased entries which would enable the show to be financially viable. Therefore, in retrospect it seems surprising that when, in 1972, Chris Lambert became secretary the position was still only part time and remained so until 1992. The appointment, in 1998, as Chris' eventual successor, of Rodger Read previously South Lakeland District Council's Chief Leisure Services officer indicated that as they moved towards their third century the Society and Show required professional expertise more than ever before. Along with changes in personnel the Society's constitution was also modified and from the 15th January 1996 it became a limited company known as 'The Westmorland County Agricultural Society Ltd'. There was now a 'Board of Directors & Planning & Development Committee' consisting of 13 members plus the chairman George Proctor and vice chairman John A. Geldard. A strict rule was that the chairman stood down after three years when he (it has only been a 'he' so far) would be replaced by the current vice-chairman. Board meetings were held about every two months to frame major policy in conjunction with recommendations made by the Light Horse Sub-Committee, the Cattle Committee and the Sheep Committee. Major decisions - and discussion - was still undertaken by the General Management Committee, meeting four times annually, composed of some 77 representatives from organisations involved in the show. The most crucial, detailed and arduous work still, however, remained the responsibility of the Field Committee.

After 200 years of door to door or farm to farm collections the Society's finances were by the 1990's more or less modernised and most subscribers including 120 Vice-Presidents now made their subscriptions by bankers order. Even so the 1998 show catalogue listed 17 collectors some of whom still found that when it came to parting with brass old Westmerian habits ran hard. In 1999 there were current tales of how one member had kept a recent collector at bay until 1 am before he handed over his £5 annual sub. With equal Westmerian stubbornness the collector got his revenge by delaying his departure for a couple more hours so that the member was kept up until 3am!

Underlying the financial, agricultural and social success of the show the weather on The Day was the crucial factor. The first post-war show got off to a good start and apart from 'two or three slight showers in the afternoon' 1946 had 'one of the few fine days in recent weeks'. Though 'sunshine was lacking the weather was fine' was the verdict in 1947 but in 1948 when a 'cold wind

**WESTMORLAND AGRICULTURAL SOCIETY MANAGEMENT COMMITTEE
1999**

Front row seated left to right:
Mrs D. Galbraith, Mr A. Duckett, Mr D.H. Fell (Treasurer), Mr F.G. Martin (President Elect), Mr R. Read (Chief Executive), Mrs D. Lambert (President), Mr J.A. Geldard (Chairman), Mrs O. Clarke OBE, Mr J.J. Park (Vice Chairman), Mr G. Procter

Second row left to right:
Mrs R. Rigg, Mr W.H. Robinson, Mr W.A. Atkinson, Mrs J.A. Clark, Mrs. J.M. Buckley, Mr M. Lambert, Mrs M.F. Wood, Mr T. Mason, Mrs M. Chapman, Mrs S. Jones, Mr J. Fishwick, Mr B. Willison, Mrs K.L. Nicholson, Mr B. Clarke

Third row left to right:
Mr T.K. Gorst, Mr C. Wildman, Mr M.H. Robinson, Mr J.H. Willison, Mr J.C. Mason, Mr. M. Johnson, Mr C. Mason, Mr G. Capstick, Mr W. Melling, Mr H. Robinson, Mr J. Robinson, Mr J. Dewhurst

Fourth row left to right:
Mr J. Bennett, Mr J.W. Todd, Mr C. Whittaker, Mr J. Garnett, Mr D.T. Jackson, Mr C. Gibson

Back row left to right:
Mr B. Barnes, Mr D. Lawrence, Mr T. Nelson, Mr C. Briggs, Mr F. Park, Mr G. Haworth, Mr J. Stott

Amongst other members of the Management Committee not in the photograph are the following officers and life members:
Mr B.E. Ellis, Mr G.E. Robinson, Mr S. Procter, Mr Sam Raymer, Mr R.H. Mason, Mr R.E. Taylor, Mr J.A. Dixon, Mr T.D. Edmondson, Mr L. Hayton

restricted the gate' the report recalled that there had been a 'heat wave' the previous year. A more acute problem typical of the age of austerity beset motorised show goers in 1948 as officials from the Petroleum Licensing Board staged a check for 'red petrol' (which could only be legally used in farm machinery) 'and during the day many private cars were inspected and found to be in breach of rationing regulations'. Though petrol was still rationed in 1949 car parking receipts at £60 were double those of the previous year and 'a glorious day and the early conclusion of harvesting brought thousands of people to the show'. It was 'dull' for the 1950 show and 'dismal with a few showers' for that of 1951. Nevertheless in 1951 9,000 spectators paid £803 to get in. Because of Foot and Mouth disease there was no show in 1952 and contrary to the general trend in the Coronation summer of 1953 there was 'brilliant weather'. Then came 1954, the first of several bad years which over the next 20 years almost brought the show to bankruptcy. Described as the worst weather on record there were strong winds and driving rain which ruined the afternoon when stock exhibitors had to remove their animals in a quagmire and child riders and leapers found the weather a bigger trial than the obstacles. At the end of the day 'a dozen tractors worked unceasingly until late evening in extricating bogged down vehicles from a sea of mud'. Even so the gate income remained steady at £802 and bumper takings of £1,360 in 'a good year' of 1955 balanced the books. 'Heavy rain on the Wednesday created mud patches' in 1957 but a further deluge held off until £1,000 had been spent on admission. This was the last year that the show was held on its pre-war site at Longlands for as the show report announced 'within a month it was learned yesterday, the first sods will be cut preparatory to the erection of the new modern school so that in future years only part of the usual showground will be available.' A shift over towards Shap road did not incommode arrangements for successive shows as thanks to Mr W. Dobson's Field Committee 'the organisation was beyond criticism and a system worked perfectly in keeping vehicles to tracks leaving general grassed areas undisturbed'. Unfortunately people 'must have stayed away to salvage rain damaged crops' and takings were down. An 'impediment' in 1959 - and it would not have been Westmorland if folk did not grumble about good as well as bad - was 'that it was 80 in the shade except that there was no shade'. Similarly in 1960 'the only complaint from the crowd touring the many attractions in shirtsleeves and summer frocks was that because of recent bad weather they were encumbered with rain coats all day'. Ninety per cent of the record crowd of 10,000 in 1962 were having to wear rubber boots and 'one woman was seen barefoot as she laboriously pushed a perambulator through the clinging mud'. The 1963 headline was 'Sunshine smiles on a gay day'. Showers marred 1964 when a 10,500 crowd ignored churned up mud but next year attendance and takings were down. Disappointment in 1965 seemed all the greater because the Society had just

The Field Committee inspects proposed cattle stalls

taken one of the most important steps in its history for after 167 years it had bought the show field. Purchased, after tortuous negotiations by the Secretary Alan Thompson and the Chairman W.P. Dobson, from the Pattinson estates this transaction proved to be one of the most profitable investments ever made in the locality for - within 25 years - the land which had cost about £6,500 realised over two million pounds! Substantial sums were however spent on improvements. For the 1966 show a field boundary wall across the site was demolished and the stone used as hard core for a track connecting the Appleby and Shap roads. A perfect day, despite three and a half inches of rain during the previous weekend, 'attracted many hundreds with no interest in agriculture' in the crowd of 10,000 who listened to a military band and craned to see a display 7,000 feet up by the Black Knight Parachutists who were 'a far cry from 1799 but it is now taken for granted that people needed something more than cows and sheep to interest them'. In 1967 they also had a display by the County Fire Brigade until it was summoned to put out a barn fire at J.B. Martindale's farm at Patton. 'Mr Martindale left the Show to assist his neighbour but when he reached the top of Patton hill he realised it was his own barn from which six calves were rescued only in the nick of time'. Sadly despite all the entertainment and excitement there was still an overdraft of £267 after the 1967 show.

Ironically - or inevitably - the urgently needed good year did not occur and the Show and Society reached their post-war depths in 1968, 1969 and 1970. The wettest morning for months meant that tractors had to pull cars on to the field in 1968 and because the river Mint was roaring in full spate at Old Field, Docker where the hounds normally crossed the river the hound trail had to be abandoned. 1969 was a wash out causing Mr J. Williams the secretary to moan 'since we bought the Show ground as a permanent home we have been planning the gradual provision of permanent facilities such as toilet blocks, and a grandstand but two bad years will mean that all our funds must go towards the continuance of the show'. As the day's takings only amounted to £676 everyone prayed for a good year in 1970. But instead in every respect the sodden depths were plumbed. An inch of rain fell on the show day and an incessant gale brought the 200 foot luncheon tent crashing down. Makeshift arrangements were made for luncheons but a wrestling match and vintage car rally were rained off and a money raising barbecue due to be held in the big tent in the evening had to be cancelled. Despite higher charges takings came to only £697. Moreover, unlike the similarly hit Grasmere Show, the County committee had not insured against a bad day. Perhaps one of the basic problems was the day itself. Whatever the weather the second Thursday in September when the schools were back and the holiday season was drawing to a close was hardly calculated to attract the general public especially 'as on the day itself everything was long over by tea time.'

'We have considered changing the date' explained Mr W.P. Dobson, the chairman, 'but', he went on to plead in a sentiment typical of the demoralisation of the 1970's, 'like everyone else these days the farming fraternity want their Saturdays free and this can apply to people who run the trade stands. In any case all other Thursdays between mid July and the end of August are taken up by some other national event'. Inevitably the *Westmorland Gazette* highlighted that the 'whole future of the Westmorland Show is causing grave concern'.

It was, therefore, with that same Dunkirk Spirit frequently used to describe the activities of show officials when they salvaged exhibits from the show ground swamps, that a group of activists led by the Chairman Harold Robinson, show field Director Tony Atkinson and the secretary Robert Sykes with Brian Ellis and Fred Downham embarked on a rescue mission involving fund raising from socials, barbecues, a sponsored walk, a 200 Club and - 'wat iver next' - Pop Festivals. Funds raised not only reduced the overdraft but enabled £1000 from the Social Committee to be invested, along with contributions from industrial sponsors, in a £2,500 permanent oval track - 'three furlongs by 50 feet'.

This quickly became home to 'Race Way' an independent syndicate for trotting events which took a three year lease for the low season to produce income which helped pay for a £6,500 grandstand in 1972.

Deservedly the sun shone on the new enterprises. From the 'sunbathed' show ground in 1971 a crowd of 12,000 saw Wing Commander Gerry Turnbull make a balloon ascent while on terra firma extra displays by Cumbria Police, Mrs O'Loughlin's Keep Fit group and of sheep dog handling by nationally famous F.W. Downham of Arkholme enthralled town and country folk alike.

Ever popular heavies: brewers' drays on show c.1975. Photo: Westmorland Gazette

Over the next years as income rose to nearly £3,000 in gate receipts alone so did the show's aims, expectations and attractions.

Although the committee frequently pleaded that 'they wished to build on the traditions of the countryside and wanted no gimmicks to attract the crowd' entertainment now ranged from a balancing act on poles, steam traction engines, Cumberland and Westmorland wrestling and - in 1975 - a performance by the 5th Inniskillin Dragoon Guards who were in town along with a whole troop of ever popular brewers' dray horses for the torchlight procession which closed the Kendal Gathering on the Friday following each show. In 1974 £8,000 had been spent on preparations and £1,500 on prize money and only a sudden thunderstorm which stopped the show jumping prevented a crowd target of 15,000 being reached. Drizzle kept numbers down to 10,000 in 1976 though there were no regrets (as the century's longest drought was over) except from Mr David Gribbon, a cattle judge from Devon, who said that Kendal was the coldest show out of fourteen at which he had judged that year. He warmed all hearts, however, by adding that despite the windswept ring the cattle were by far the best he had ever seen. Although some tents were blown down in the night

15,000 people turned up for the 1979 show. With steady all round improvement over the next years the mirage of a crowd estimated at between 18,000 and 20,000 was achieved in 1981. In that year the weather was so dry that the fire brigade had to douse dust storms stirred up from the limestone gravel base of the trotting track 'which threatened to eclipse the event in clouds of choking white fumes'. Disaster was averted in 1982 only at the last minute when the various authorities were prevailed upon to come together to suspend sewer digging works on Shap Road which would have blocked all the major accesses to the field for what was another record show. Damp weather caused attendance to fall to below 15,000 in 1983 when champion wrestlers Allan T. Irving (boys), Tom Harrington (11-18) and Harry Brockbank (all weights) 'won in the rain'. The milk quota furore had also contributed to a drop by a third in cattle entries. Herdsmen who attended were, however, heartened by Michael Jopling's 'glowing tribute to Cumbrain (sic!) farmers having the best stock in the country.'

1983 was only a blip and most of the shows in the 1980's faced the reverse of the old dilemma. With better marketing and facilities on which £40,000 had been spent on field tracks alone, the shows had become too big and too successful to be easily accommodated on the show ground.

In particular the trade stands both in space occupied and income generated now constituted an important part of the show. Shortages and travel difficulties

Seeming more spacious than was made out. Trade Section 1977

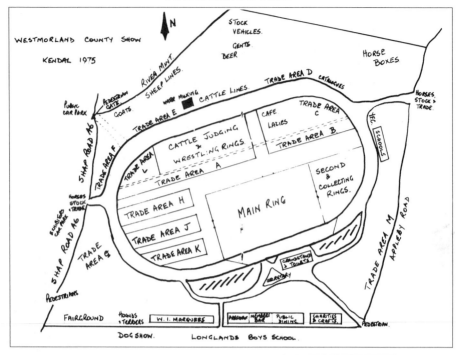

Plan of the Kendal show field 1975

had kept a commercial interest to a minimum in the immediate post-war years but by the late 1940's commercial enterprise was reviving. Electricity was laid on for traders in 1949 and in 1950 with petrol restrictions easing there were said to be half a mile of stands. By 1975 Chris Lambert delightedly announced that trade stands had doubled to 160 in his first two years as secretary. Only 50 were 'agricultural'; other stands ranged from 'tiny sweet stalls to the articulated lorry caravans of the major banks and car manufacturers'. Applications came from as far away as central Scotland and Somerset. Ten years later Chris was having to turn away up to a hundred franchise paying traders and for those who attended there was 'not an inch between the 190 stands on the field'. More importantly there was not enough room for the raison d'être of the whole enterprise. Cattle and sheep entries were up by nearly 100% on previous lean years, horses had trebled, goats were up from 38 in 1972 to 235 in 1990 while the Dog Show (held concurrently with the main show) which counted for little or nothing in the immediate post-war years, now had hundreds of entries. Though older cattle and sheep men on the committee might be loath to admit it these newer classes were amongst the most popular with the paying public. Moreover although the crowds continued to be big with 17,000 in 1988 and 1989

Aerial view of the 'Kendal' show c.1980

there was evidence that the prospect of having to face a time consuming snarl up in Kendal's traffic jams was keeping many people away. There were even fears for safety of the crowd. An escaped bull had caused twenty minutes of chaos in 1989 and elicited questions as to how the emergency services might cope with a packed field and jammed streets if a more serious accident occurred. Car parking was now an almost insuperable problem as most of the last remaining suitable fields were covered by the new Garden House estate. Vandalism was also becoming such a menace, with marquees being slashed and guy ropes cut on the night before the show, that the secretary warned that a barbed wire fence might have to be erected around the field.

Ironically the solution came from the heart of the problem - the show ground's proximity to the growing town of Kendal. The town was, statistically, one of the most prosperous in the kingdom and, as all over the country, there was a demand for 'out of town' shopping. The time was just right: ten years earlier the site would not have been needed; ten years later planning permission for its development would have been difficult. Thus in circumstances which are not yet clear or fully disclosed pragmatists on the committee jumped at the chance to sell the showfield site to a superstore. Rumours abounding at the 1989 show that it would be the last on the old field had been dispelled by the Chairman Fred Martin but shortly afterwards news broke that a deal had been struck by the Society's new solicitor Len Hayton and Revivals Properties, a company which was backing Morrison's Superstore. After skilful negotiations led for the Society by Len Hayton (who got the original offer more than doubled!) the Committee decided to accept £2.6m for the field providing an alternative site for the show could be found.

Then the uproar started. Tempers were lost on all sides and tears were even shed by tough men who had devoted decades in building up the facilities on the Kendal field. Noisy packed out meetings were held and there was general sympathy felt for some formerly loyal supporters of the show when they were excluded from attending the main decision making meeting because technically they were not members of the Society. Nevertheless by a vote of 102 votes to 30 the members decided to sell the field even though it would probably mean a move away from Kendal. As a result threats to boycott any show anywhere else were wholesale; scores of letters reached the press protesting at the abandonment of what many still called 'Kendal Show'. Opponents to the scheme included Pat Stamp, local branch Chairman of the National Farmers Union who believed that a move from Kendal would 'cause problems for other groups and lead to the creation of another industrial site'. Controversy polarised around leading farmers: John Richardson declared 'the credibility of the society is at risk in our selfish efforts to secure a crock of gold'. Chairman of the trustees Brian Ellis's response was 'don't let's be Luddites. Don't let's look back and say things must never change'. Kendal Town Council whose arguments were bound up with the 'out of town shopping' controversy passed a resolution against the move while South Lakeland District Council raised the issue in full Council as well as in its planning committee. The Liberal Party, currently in the ascendant in Kendal, muscled in on the side of the opponents and quickly secured several thousand signatures to a petition against any move as it 'would make Kendal a more faceless place'. This caused farmer Robert Bell to query 'if any people who signed the petition were offered a million pounds to secure their family's future, I wonder what they would do?' The Conservatives were divided on the issue and there was trouble at the Constituency Executive Council when a 'Kendal' Show diehard tried to introduce a resolution against the move and also to involve the Member of Parliament. Here, however, the proponents of the view that the County Show belonged to the whole county and not just to Kendal won the day but many decent folk were still left with hurt feelings. Perhaps the Women's Institutes were more pragmatic: they said they would go wherever the show went.

'Where to go' was the main problem. With at least a million pounds at their disposal money was not a problem compared to locality and planning permission. Seven sites in all were considered and detailed schemes were drawn up for potential show fields at Carus Green on Burneside Road; Middleshaw, Old Hutton; by the A6 at Prizet south of Kendal and, in conjunction with a possible leisure park, on the old race course at Scout Scar close to the western bypass. All in turn were rejected by either the Committee or the planners while a much reported scheme to purchase the Carus Green land as a site for secondary activities like riding events also came to nothing. Eventually a site to the north of Endmoor was selected. Situated on the main road, only five miles from Kendal and close to the M6 it was well suited to the purpose although much levelling and drainage would be required. Unfortunately this site lacked permanent buildings and it was outside the line of 'permitted development'. Despite offers of planning gain in the form of various sports facilities there was mixed opinion in the local Parish Council of Preston Richard and after a year of wrangling it was thrown out by the District Council and also after an appeal by the Ministry of the Environment.

The Committee then decided to go for Lanes Farm in Preston Patrick, only a mile away from Endmoor, on the Crooklands-Milnthorpe road. At first glance this site was not ideal as to get to it drivers would either have to cross a narrow bridge over the canal at Crooklands or twist through the traffic lights at Milnthorpe and then negotiate another awkward bridge at Milton Moor. In addition the main part of the proposed show field was rather cramped and both sides of the Milnthorpe road and of the lane to Stainton would have to be used for parking. On the other hand at around £700,000 it was relatively cheap and there were sufficient buildings to accommodate the Society's offices and meeting rooms and the farmhouse would provide an on-site home for the secretary. It was also believed, not altogether accurately, that as the fields were underlain with gravel, drainage would be no problem.

Difficulties apart and with the objections brushed aside from Milnthorpe Parish Council that their village would be gridlocked on show days the plans for the show field were passed and after 192 years the County Show moved out of Kendal. Apart from the adaptation of the buildings and improvements to entrances no major capital works such as grandstands were undertaken on the new field which initially was to be used just on show day. Eventually, after the purchase of additional land from Milton House farm (making an entire holding of 84 acres), extra events began to be held on the edge of the main show field. By the late 1990's equestrian activities organised by such bodies as the Lake District Riding Club, the Northern Show Pony Society and Oxenholme Pony Club were held on most weekends from May to September.

The infrastructure of the main ground was also improved. Water and mains sewerage were installed so that instead of the traditional (and noxious) 'back in

Even the detractors of the new show site had to admit that there was more room for parking at Crooklands. Photo: Westmorland Gazette

and pull out' temporary conveniences the Ladies at least could have 'real flush toilets'. Above all £50,000 was invested in permanent roads which did away with the Field Committee's having to hire temporary aluminium 'Eve Trakway' at a cost of over £10,000 per annum.

For the first Crooklands Show in 1991, despite the threats at boycotting, entries were well up to target and the show was judged 'a huge success with people still coming on to the field at 2.30pm'. Most of the 'waverers' had returned by 1992 when there were visitors from all over the country. Moreover it was now claimed that there were no problems of site access with more entrances especially for the trade stands which were now served by mains electricity.

Along with trade stand demonstrations and displays were now well to the fore. A tentative introduction to non agricultural or domestic displays had been begun in 1950 when owing to there being no Women's Institute tent there were demonstrations 'under the auspices' (as the phrase was) of an organisation calling itself 'the Rural Industries Committee of the National Council for Social Service' which displayed 'oak spale and willow basket making, pottery with a potter's wheel, hand loom weaving and engineering'.

To 'encourage the men' a prize class for shepherd's crooks was introduced in 1966. For many years the main winners were W.R. Steele of Windermere and Mr Harper of Sedbergh but other competitors, notably J.S. Williamson and R. Wightman, came in when the classes expanded to include such variants as 'horn headed, wooden headed, ornamental horn headed, thumb stick and stick for a Lady'. From then on there was no holding back the non-agricultural element though as late as 1987 the Chief Steward Brian Ellis was still asserting that 'we pride ourselves on being an agricultural show and not a fair'. By 1995 it was even reported that for 'most (!) of the visitors to the Show the main attraction was the town in miniature where trade stands hawked their wares from farming machinery to small charity stalls.' The next year the 'Made in Cumbria' marquee was hailed as 'putting modern town centres to shame'. Amongst a conglomeration of bodgers, weavers, wheelwrights, cloggers, thatchers, blacksmiths, beeswax makers and stalls vending anything from dolls to the 'saucy stickers announcing that Young Farmers do it in wellies' there was a cheese stall where passers by were invited to don a blindfold in order to guess varieties of cheese. While the artistic could admire lace making and 'cane bottoming' the macho could demonstrate their prowess by pitch forking a truss of hay over a bar or by using a sledge hammer to raise a weight to ring a bell. Despite all the blather no one really forgot that they came to an agricultural show of national renown. In 1993 the sheep classes attracted 600 which according to the chief steward Brian Clarke was the highest for any one day show in the country - ever! 'Mud and more mud' did not keep attendance down in 1994 and in 1995, 1996 and 1997 crowds were estimated at more than 17,000 and only slightly less in 1998 when in the tradition of the old 'Kendal Show' it rained all day at Crooklands.

Because of the uncertainty - or perhaps the certainty - of the wet Westmorland climate craft, domestic and produce marquees provided a welcome sheltered attraction. Having evolved from the sections allocated to the 'butter ladies' before the war the domestic classes in the 1940's and 1950's still had an old fashioned air about them. An austerity note was struck in 1946 when there was a prize - won by Mrs J. Batty of Old Hutton - for a loaf of National Flour but there was also a class for traditional oat cakes won by 'Mrs Jennings and son'. Along with home baking there were well entered classes for white and brown hens, duck and goose eggs but butter was not a patch on former times. Even so it was a notable achievement when nine year old Miss M. James of Hincaster won a first for butter in 1953. Sometimes the farmer's wife could outdo the show successes of her husband and in 1965 Mrs E. Lambert of Lindeth Farm, Winster, 'wife of Mr Herbert Lambert the well known farmer', won three gold stars for 'wine, raspberry and strawberry jam and silver stars for jelly, dressed fowl and floribunda roses'. That 'Olde Tyme Fayre' still appealed to modern youth was shown in 1966 'when the exhibitors in the food stuffs section were shocked when they returned to their stands at the end of the afternoon to find that bread

Exhibition of the work of the nimble fingers of the W.I.

and confectionery had been looted by a gang of youths.' More positively the show's domestic classes kept alive traditional skills in a 'take away' age with for instance yeast cookery attracting record entries in 1992.

More than anywhere else it was at the County Show that Westmorland's Women's Institutes manifested their commitment to their motto of 'For Home and Country' by preserving, popularising and above all developing the skills of rural women and through them those of their children and menfolk. Already in 1946 the 'Women's Institute tent attracted much attention' when the winning entries all for produce came from Underbarrow, Crosscrake, Garth Row and Skelsmergh, Burton, Appleby and Killington WI's. A handicrafts section started in a small way in 1947 and after a gap in 1950 there were three hundred entries in 1951. In 1953 came the first co-operative class (in which items were made by several members) when Outgate WI with 97% produced the winning entry for 'a meal for two'. Later the co-operative sections had to be created by at least eight members and there were classes for institutes with more or less than 40 members all of which exemplified the originality and talent (especially in display) of the members of this remarkable organisation. Oddly for a stock

W.I. trophies

farming area there was a very early display in 1955 of 'vegetarianism' when the co-operative was for a 'meatless lunch' which was won by Natland; altogether, in that year, 140 members drawn from every institute in the Westmorland Federation put in 294 entries. In 1958 there were 850 entries 'though on this occasion there were no handicrafts' but the co-operative Old Fashioned Farmhouse Tea was popular and 'as a result many dishes and cutlery and decorations customary in Westmorland farmhouses of the last century were on display'. The tea was won by Old Hutton which in 1959 won again with Silver Wedding. Garth Row and Skelsmergh won with a Halloween supper for six 'with ghost like figures playing their gruesome part in the nocturnal spread'. In 1960 when Ravenstonedale won there was again a youthful theme with 'a meal for six for 17 year old young people where spectacular and appetising items were on display'. 'Oranges and Lemons' was won by Winster, the third co-operative win in succession in 1960. Craft seems from then on to have been added to cookery and co-operative topics displayed included in 1968 'Our Golden Jubilee' won by Staveley, 1969 10 gifts for Christmas morning (Ravenstonedale and Newbiggin), 1970 'a country festival' (Crook with Kendal market but Casterton's Threshing Day attracted attention with a real steam engine), 1974 'Family Celebration' (Underbarrow with the 'Return of the native'), 1975 'the good earth' (Rydal), 1981 'store cupboard' (Rydal), 1988 'Made in Britain' (Staveley), 1991 'a Taste of Cumbria' with nettle beer, sticky toffee pudding and potted char (Finsthwaite) and in 1994 a 'Murder on the Orient Express' co-operative was won by Windermere with a display 'mixing good food with artistic genius'. Not everyone, however, was as complimentary about Windermere judging by a reported snatch of conversation: 'You can tell it's Windermere' remarked one passer by, eyeing up the silverware, damask, Waterford crystal and very authentic OE boarding cards 'Plenty of money there!' Perhaps the Federation officials took note for next year - the 50th anniversary of VE Day - the co-operative theme was wartime rations when spartan fare like carrot cake and Woolton pie were on display along with such wartime culinary aids as hay box ovens and a canning machine. To commemorate a more important anniversary for the WI - the Centenary in 1997 of the foundation of the first

Institute at Stony Creek, in Canada - the exhibition's theme was Canadian. Among an array of nineteenth century artefacts on display were examples of rag rugs, a fire screen of pressed flowers, 'a hardanger counted thread cushion cover and a silk scarf printed with maple leaves'.

Over the years the Women's Institutes' entries proliferated almost annually so that by 1977 there were 2,500 entries staged in two enormous marquees. In 1979 a queuing system had to be organised in the tents and in 1981 following the death of the long term organiser Miss K.M. Kelly entries had to be reduced by 200 just to enable her successors to cope. As in other aspects of the show a leading organiser was Mrs Olive Clarke who in 1987 after staging a huge exhibition (which took two days to judge) of 1,000 handicrafts ranging through basketry, crocheting, embroidery to metal work and word processing declared that 'you can go to the length and breadth of the country and not see a better show'. Occasionally when handicraft entries dropped there were worries that old skills were losing ground. In 1996 Mrs Martin 'wondered whether the old British pastime of knitting seems to be passing away' but the next year a display of 'combined knitting' featuring a knitted town of 'much knitting on the needle' and its smaller hamlet of 'lesser knitting' by Kendal ladies dispelled such fears. Westmorland still knew how to cook and in 1992 the Chairman Mrs Joan Bentley said that 'even though the recession was digging deep members still

Rydal W.I. winning co-operative effort for 'The good old days', 1981

146

managed to produce 60 rich fruit cakes which would cost around £4 to make'. A sign of changing society was shown, however, in the popularity of a new class called 'cooking alone'. That the WI's had come a long way from the old insular jam and Jerusalem image was confirmed in 1996 by an exhibit for the International Association for Country Women of the World which contained 'Mexican Tacos, Indian head dresses, South American artefacts, Indian stir fry and African savoury tabouleh'. A sweetly feminine flavour still persisted for a sugar craft class was introduced in 1991 when Mrs R. Phizacklea's apricot coloured posy and Mrs Wood's selection of orchids won top marks but the judge Mrs Nora Brough said the wires in the flowers rendered them inedible. This opinion was irrelevant as everyone judged them to be too good to eat anyway.

For Westmorland's country women the show provided an opportunity to demonstrate and extend their personal skills for which if they were successful they would be rewarded not by cash prizes but by stars. A few trophies like the Clarke Cup and the Mrs Appleby Cup were also awarded to institutes whose members had won the highest points and stars. Literally scores of clever women were singled out for praise by the *Westmorland Gazette* in its show reports. Representative champion crafts women included the Misses Whittle of Beetham

for handicrafts in 1955, Mrs E. Brownlee of Heversham who scored 99% for embroidery on canvas in 1962, Mrs J. Sowerby of Preston Patrick - a long serving 'champion' - who swept the board with her embroidered place mats in 1971, an embroidery of Heversham church in 1989 and with her quilt in 1991, Mrs Todd of Rydal for tapestry seat covers in 1987, Mrs Hilda Gladstone (one of the mainstays of the produce section) who at the age of 74 won 4 gold stars for cookery in 1990, Mrs Stott and Mrs Nelson of Lupton for rush chairs in 1991 and Mrs P.D. Hacking of Arnside with clown dolls in 1996. Not least of the Women's Institute members' skill lay in their ability to set up their mammoth displays. In 1993 an early bird reporter

Mrs Hilda Gladstone (right), president 1992 with Mrs Nora Willisson (left), wife of chairman Henry Willisson

Winners of the Gazette shield 1961. Wilson Melling, Nora Wilson, Brian Horn

noticed 'that long before dawn breaks the WI members creep over the show field armed with torches and their labours of love'. Quite often they had to cope with near disaster. In 1995 there were only 100 entries in 'on the night before' but then 'as if by magic exquisite patchwork quilts, pewter, decoupage, and every form of handiwork flooded in by the hundred' making 600 entries - 100 up on the previous year. In 1998 there were so many entries that they had to be taken two days before the show to Preston Patrick Memorial Hall for judging. Then on the show morning the carrier booked to convey the exhibits to the show ground did not turn up; so with true 'Dunkirk Spirit' everybody got cars to transport precious things: 'chairs, coffee tables, metal work, most beautiful needlework, a wedding dress, samples of a 'Taste of Britain' including a hogshead joined by a brown trout, shortbread and trifle to demonstrate England's green and pleasant land' were got to the muddy field on time by the indomitable WI ladies.

Many of the successful Women's Institute members had developed their skills and obtained their competitive confidence (and in many cases their husbands) in the Young Farmers Clubs for whom the show was the 'big day'. The YFC's were also important in providing the Society with new - human - stock. As the Rev. Jim Johnston - formerly the Society's Treasurer (when he was a bankmanager, and not a parson) said when he was President of the Show in

1988, 'it was down to the continued interests of Young Farmers Club whose members eventually gravitated to the Show's management that enabled the committee to obtain fresh blood.' They also, he added, 'formed a happy marriage between town and country'. Certainly looking back on the second half of the twentieth century many members of the teams which won the *Westmorland Gazette* Challenge Shield for stock judging went on to become successful farmers though not all became staunch show supporters. Thus the Orton number one team which won in 1946 comprised R.W. and E. Huck and R.J. Bainbridge while in Kent Estuary the runners up included J.A. Gibson, C.S. Mason and J.F. Pickthall, all of whom became exceptionally prominent in agriculture and local affairs. There were still, and for long afterwards, separate show classes for girl young farmers and much was made of the YFC handicrafts in 1947 when the main individual winners were Margaret and Vera Webster. Amongst the usual knitting, embroidery and needlework was a class, typical of the make do and mend age of austerity, for 'adaptation' - making a new garment out of an old one. But male chauvinism was shifting - a little - and Audrey Townsend was a member of the winning Kirkby Stephen team in 1948. Even so it was still a matter for comment when nine years later Nora Stott was a member along with John Galbraith and Edward Todd of the successful Preston Patrick team. Later top stock women included Nora Wilson who with E.W. Melling and B. Horn was part of the top Preston Patrick B team in 1961 and Hazel Fawcett who with Thomas Dobson and John Inman won for Crosthwaite in 1969. Historical continuity was demonstrated when Crook B team won in 1970 as two

of its members Frank and James Park were nephews of the winners of the first pre-war competition while the third member of the team John Geldard went on to become a leading member of the Show Committee. The members of the winning team were now invariably several years younger than earlier competitors. When Kent Estuary B team won in 1954 the ages of team members were reported as being: Henry Martin 19, John Pickthall 24 and Peter Handley 22. Over the years many YFC's had an 'A' and 'B' team and Lunesdale, for instance, quite often entered a 'C' team until in the early seventies it was thought that judging for the *Gazette* Shield took too long. So in 1974 the team event was replaced by a chauvinistically named 'Stockman' of the year judging competition when the winner of the old shield for the new competition was Neil Dowker of Milnthorpe. Several stock 'men' won twice including Graham Galbraith of Preston Patrick in 1978 and 1981 and John Benson of Crook in 1986 and 1987.

By the 1980's the YFC's contribution to the show had become more varied and also more light hearted with 'It's a knock out' competitions and parades of decorated floats. The floats class was a good way of ensuring that YFC's had their entry ready on time for the next night's Torch Light Parade but with so much to do there were never more than seven floats available to parade on Show Day. For many years the top float was won by Grayrigg YFC which in 1979 won the overall competition for the Kendal Gathering with a starkly scatological depiction of the country vet soap opera 'All Creatures Great and Small'.

'The Westmorland County Show is our shop window' was the verdict of Carol Galbraith the steward of the YFC craft tent in 1979. She might have added that YFC's also provided a vital side of social life for young rural people deprived of much of the entertainment routinely available to town dwellers. More seriously they promoted an introduction to affairs and the skills required to take part in public life. Thus at more recent shows the YFC's prizes for discussion groups and debating competitions were awarded while their enormous contribution to charities such as Riding for the Disabled have been acknowledged. Moreover from time to time Westmorland Young Farmers have entertained many overseas visitors especially from their 'twin' area of Rheinisch Bergischer Kress.

Life for YFC's is not always made up of earnest endeavour, not that entertainment was necessarily light. Hence in 1990 'the World Bale Rolling Championships' were held on the show field. In the heats the 'world record' was broken by Neil Barrow of Rusland and Brian Horn of Grayrigg though they could not repeat the achievement in the finals when the bale to be rolled weighed 300 kg (600lbs) and measured '5ft 3ins across and 4ft wide'. Moreover two of the rollers were young ladies Jane Geldard of Lowick and Christine Nelson of Ravenstonedale. Never had the genetic equality amongst human participants of the show been better demonstrated, nor how far Westmorland farming folk had come from the more socially sedate days of pre-war years let alone 1799.

Even when they were at the height of their popularity in the 1950's and 1960's very few young Westmerians actually belonged to a Young Farmers Club. But they all went to school. Although the YFC craft display had included an exhibit from Kendal (girls) High School as far back as 1946 there were no separate exhibitions until a display of art work was shown in 1959 when 'there were many appreciative comments'. A 'How Now Brown Cow' mural painted by pupils of Longlands Girls Modern School superintended by Miss J. Varley 'the art

Popular non-agricultural attractions included
'Transport through the ages.' 1965 Photo: *Westmorland Gazette*

mistress' (*sic*) was on view at the 1968 show. These, however, were one off affairs and only in 1970 was there a tent, arranged by Mrs Owen of Kendal, 'displaying the artistic achievements of children attending local schools' which featured a pottery demonstration by Kendal (boys) Grammar School.

The early displays set the pattern. Despite all the variations in school syllabi the overwhelming impression conveyed by the schools' tent (at least to pedants) was that arts and crafts dominated pupils' studies. No one in fact minded at all and much delight was aroused in 1973, for instance, by self portraits painted by every child in Underbarrow Primary School and a Roman Gladiator made by P. Wells from Kendal Grammar School. The most popular exhibit in the 'vast schools' tent in 1974 was a design by Frances Birch of Kendal High School for a badge for the show which incorporated in three equal sections a cow, a sheep and a pig. Pigs were not altogether appropriate as there were no pigs at the show. Indeed when 28 pigs were exhibited by the Rare Breeds Society at the 1983 show it was believed that it was the first time since the war. Thereafter, though they were always loved by the crowd, swine have only appeared sporadically.

Farming and the rural landscape have been well depicted by the schools. Cartmel Priory School 'had a hard hitting display of the vital importance of grass' in 1974 and Langdale a giant landscape in 1975. Langdale sheep farming appeared in 1977 when, also, nettle soup was on the menu from Milnthorpe Modern. In 1978 Milnthorpe pupils dispensed seaweed cake though the drop

One of the societies' sponsored farm visits for primary schools, Grayrigg 1997

scones, pancakes and apple fritters baked by Longlands Boys were better appreciated by the tasters. Much of the imagination behind the entries, which despite the inevitable emphasis on display really did have a cross curricular theme, was due to the professional expertise of the schools tent organiser Stephen Barratt. Memorable examples of schools' skills included the Leven Valley School's 'Bayeux' tapestry of its first 25 years' history in 1977, a demonstration of each stage in the construction of Queen Katherine School's prize winning 'Egyptian' float in 1980 and roller skating to pop music, again by Queen Katherine School, in 1981. Not surprisingly one visitor was reported as saying 'school was never like this in my day'. Under the direction of Mrs Olive Clarke, assisted later on by the former YFC organiser David Lawson, the schools' tent became an even more important part of the show displaying work from special as well as mainstream schools, from local colleges and by students working for other courses particularly the Duke of Edinburgh's Award Scheme. To cope with the expansion the tent grew 'from seven poles to ten poles' which was just as well when Settlebeck School, Sedbergh exhibited a hovercraft in 1992. An heritage aspect, encouraged no doubt by the old photographs drawn from the local collection in Kendal public library (exhibited annually at the show from the 1970's onwards by Christine Strickland), also rubbed shoulders with the pupils' up to date or futuristic exhibits. Hence alongside an array of crafts including platform shoes and a quilted dress from Lakes School, a curving wine rack and painted screen from Queen Katherine's School and Greek pottery from St. Patrick's School, Endmoor there was an evocative collage of pictures of Dean Gibson School which was celebrating its centenary in 1998.

The Society's direct involvement in education expanded following the move of its headquarters to Crooklands where the converted farm buildings provided excellent lecture and meeting rooms. Seminars for both primary and secondary school teachers were organised by Muriel Wilkinson, the Society's Schools Liaison officer and the Rural Links Committee chaired by Roger Mason. To enable staff to attend the Society agreed to meet the cost of supply teacher cover which at £100 per 'released' teacher amounted to up to £3,000 for one day. As well as adding to the skills and knowledge of often urban educated teachers a multitude of cross curricular themes have been developed based on, for example, studies of the rivers Bela and Kent and on the inevitably popular farm visits. Chris Lambert, as in so much else, had pioneered the Society's links with schools and as soon as he went to live on the Show field he became a governor of nearby Milnthorpe Primary School. Chris was the first to realise that education was a two way process and it was particularly appropriate that as a memorial to him the Society established in 1998 'the Chris Lambert Bursary' to finance overseers' educational travel by local Young Farmers. In the late 1990's the Society also covered the costs for two members of the YFC's to attend the annual January farming conference held at Oxford University. It was, however, an imperative condition that those attending had to give a formal report on their return: the advancement of agriculture was, after all, the Society's principal objective.

The show - created by and for farmers and still run by them - remained, also, after 200 years primarily an agricultural show although for most of the post-war period the word 'agricultural' tended to be omitted from its title in press accounts. As in the pre-war period relatively little attention was paid to the basis of husbandry, crops, general stock and cultivation although the William Atkinson cup (for these categories) was by far the largest in size of any of the show's trophies. In 1961 'the William Atkinson' actually went to another William Atkinson of Crosslands. Other winners of this and similar best managed farm classes tended to come from the south of the Kendal's district and included the Atkinsons of Farleton, Robinsons of Preston Patrick, J.R. Mason of Rowell, W. Garnett of Ackenthwaite, H.T. Leeming of Old Hall, Dalton and W. Duckett and Son - later just A. Duckett of Coat Green. Winners from the central and northern area included over the years F.J. Jennings of Skelsmergh, A. Atkinson of Old Hutton, R. Willison of Underbarrow, T.E. Clark of Kirkby Lonsdale, T.A. Chapman of Helsington, J.N. Bowes of Crook and John Harrison of Penrith.

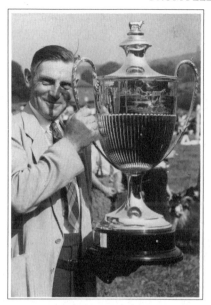 

'Big winners'
Billy Duckett c.1960 and Tony Duckett c.1980 of Coat Green with
the Atkinson Cup

Although in the 1940's bread grain was still important elsewhere in the country animal feed crops were to fore in Westmorland and at the 1946 show root crop prizes were awarded for three types of turnips, swedes, mangels and long red

mangels. Vegetables also produced champion exhibitors of whom the most prominent in the immediate post-war period was J.H. Jackson of Bela House, Beetham. In 1950 for instance 'Uncle Jack' won with round potatoes, kidney potatoes, any other variety of potato, immune, two varieties, carrots, beetroot, cabbages and vegetable marrows. Later more exotic culinary flourishes such as giant leeks and the like were on display along with

Champion breeder and judge Billy Richardson of Laverock Bridge, 1972 show   Photo: Westmorland Gazette

Shorthorns still to the fore at The Grand Parade 1967

innumerable pot plants, blooms and flower arrangements.

'The best show of cattle seen in the north'. This was the verdict on the 1950 show and indicated that despite continuing austerity things were getting back to normal. Moreover the 'instructions for judges' which applied throughout the period as contained in the 1998 catalogue continued to meet the aims of the founders of two centuries earlier: 'the object of this Show is to promote improvement in the Breeding of Stock. As regards the Classes for Cattle and Sheep, the Judges will consider the relative merits of each animal for the purpose of breeding, and not

Mr J. Hutchinson judging best group of dairy shorthorns 1959
Photo: Farmers Weekly

their present value to the butcher. In the Classes for Horses, the Judges, in addition to symmetry, will take activity and strength into consideration'.

The cattle in the first post-war shows indicated a return almost to the turn of the century as Shorthorns still dominated the show ring. But there were some new exhibitors on the scene notably W. Parsons of Overthwaite, Beetham, W.J. Dent of Kaber Fold, Kirkby Stephen and Messrs J.R. Harrison of Crossrigg, Cliburn. In the four open classes Mr Parsons won cow or heifer in calf, cow or heifer in milk. Pedigree in milk calved before 1942 was won by W. Dobson of Burton, calved after 1943, by J. Robinson of Holmescales while the still prized John Handley Memorial cup for the champion male went to R.H. Richardson. In 1947 J. Harrison was doubly successful but the highest praise was reserved for W. Parson's four year old roan cow and A.T. Dobson's pedigree yearling 'Prizet Wild Warrior'. For the first time in 1948 all the entries came from pedigree herds but there were still only six general cattle classes: Pedigree Dairy Shorthorn, Northern Dairy Shorthorn, British Friesian, Ayrshires, Special and Small Farmers. For several years the winner of the latter class always with Shorthorns was W. Richardson of Laverock Bridge. In 1950 he not only won with his bull 'Waterloo', but also obtained the Shorthorn Society's Pedigree medal. In 1948 the male champion was W.J. Dent's 'Kaber Fold Prince' whose dam was a 1,200 gallon champion. According to contemporaries such a high yield was virtually unprecedented at the time. Over the next decade or so notable successes for the Parsons, Harrison and Dent trio included: for Mr Parsons, a shorthorn which had never previously been shown in 1950, a seven year old Northern Shorthorn 'Arrogant Duchess' in 1953, and non pedigree championships for many years in the middle 1950's. Mr Harrison won the John Handley cup while the Dents father (and son after 1951) scored with Kaber Fold: 'Viscount 4th', 'Rosette' in the late 1940's, 'Prince' 1950, 'Seraphim' and 'Dolly xv' 1950. Another branch of the Dent family from Bishop Auckland entered the Shorthorn lists and, in particular, won the 1956 championship with a beast that had earlier won at the Royal Show at Newcastle. Other successful Shorthorn breeders at this time were E. Jackson of Stainton, Penrith, J.T. Grisedale, Millness Hall, R. Willison, Tullithwaite, J.G. Bell of Newby, James Holme of Hackforth, D. Wilson of Holker, and J. Hall from Barnard Castle. By the late fifties Shorthorn entries were 'not a patch' on those of more glorious times. Even so Shorthorns had a good show in 1960 when the John Handley went to T.N. Hill of Wigton with other good entries from E. and J. Robinson of Farleton (with 'Kiln Hall Sunbeam') and T.W. Crook (with 'Latterbarrow Pedro'). In 1961 there were 75 female entries and in 1962 67 beasts were entered for the Pedigree class and 64 for the Northern when once more the Dents won with 'Kaber Fold Viscount 27th'. Then in 1963 there came 'a surprising reduction': 37 entries only for the Pedigree class and 38 for the Northern. Four years later there were no entries for bulls and the combined

Above: *Mrs M. Parsons with champion female 1957*

**The Parsons of Overthwaite
like father, like mother,
like son, like daughter**
Photos: *Westmorland Gazette*

Top left:
W. Parsons with champion Friesian female 'Guilly Hill Shirley' 1965

Middle left:
Bernard Parsons with non-pedigree champion female 1956

Bottom left:
Moyra Parsons with 'Guilly Hill Shirley' 1966

Shorthorn entry was a mere 19. It seemed to be the end of the road for showing purposes for the breed. But confounding the pessimists new competitors appeared such as J. Charnley and Sons from Glasson Dock while older breeders persisted like H.E. Helme of Ormathwaite, G.W. Taylor of Crook, T.W. Blades of Crook, B. Walling of Crosthwaite, and W. Jackson of Wreay. W. Parsons went over to other breeds in the 1960's but the Dents continued with Shorthorns and by 1983 their championship wins were well into double figures. By then, however, Shorthorns virtually constituted a rare breed. In 1974 it was announced that there were only nine Shorthorn herds left in the country - most of which appeared to come from the Westmorland Show's district! Of these one of the largest with 84 cattle belonged to W.A. Robinson of Strickley, New Hutton who with the Dents and occasionally the Dobsons of Underbarrow took most of the Shorthorn prizes in the 1980's and 1990's while P.N. Coup won the, once more awarded, Handley 'piece of silver' in 1998. Mr Willie Robinson perhaps deserved a special prize for family constancy as when he won the Shorthorn championship in 1987 he was able to display a similar prize card awarded to his grandfather in 1875.

Friesians were the cause of the decline, though as it turned out not for the extinction of Shorthorns. Seven Friesian classes attracted entries from a wide area at the 1946 show when also, they did particularly well in the milk recorded classes. With exceptions like J. Parsons, W. Parsons and H. Bell, of Holme most of the winners were from out of the immediate Kendal district and included W. Kelsall of Quernmore, I.W. Airey of Roanhead, R. Fell of Barrow, and C. Chapman of Saxton Grange, Tadcaster. Two of the more local Friesian winners were ladies Mrs P. W. Manz-Fee of Staveley, who with her husband won the best female in 1948, and Mrs R. Loxham of Eden Brook, Carnforth who won the male championship in 1949. A year or two later Friesian entries from newer breeders around the Kendal district came from L. Fuller of Helsington, R. Houghton of Carnforth, T.B. Jackson of Borwick, G.W. Robinson of Farleton and, from further away, F. Philipson of Ulverston and W. Postlethwaite and Sons of Stank Farm, Barrow in Furness. Main prizes were, however, still going out of the district to R.J. Burnihope of Durham, E.F. Oswell of Winsford and R.H. Ford of Sandhutton, York. Quite quickly in the middle 1950's Friesian cattle from local herds began to win renown. In 1953 R.J. Gladstone from Middle Foulshaw won with 'Holmside Maradema', a two year old bull which had previously won at the Great Yorkshire, Highland, Chester and Otley shows. Twelve months later when he won again at Kendal the same bull had achieved 28 firsts. Many of the finest Friesians were bred on the South Westmorland plain between Kendal and the Lancashire border. Notable beasts included W. Duckett's best three females from Coat Green in 1955. In 1956 one of Mr Duckett's cows obtained a second only twelve hours after calving. H.H. Bell's 'Irton Jeans Path', from Holme Park, 'a magnificent four year old cow which has taken the premier award at Lancaster, Burton, Bentham and Kirkby Lonsdale' won for H.H. Bell of Holme Park in 1958 when the reserve went to J.W. Melling of Crosby Lodge, Milnthorpe. 'Irton Jeans Path' won the top award the next year although she was challenged by her shippon mate 'Holmland le Anderson'. From Low Sizergh H. Lancaster's cows also had a good run with highlighted wins in 1958 and 1960. In 1960 when with 98 cattle on show Friesians outnumbered Shorthorns for the first time the main winners were R.J.Gladstone, H.H. Bell, J.R. Mason of Lower Rowell, Mrs J.M. Robinson and Sons, Moss End, but the male champion belonged to W.S. Waring of Hesking near Chorley. An exceptional winner was an eight year old dry cow of Mr Gladstone 'which he brought from his native Durham and it contains a good deal of Helmside blood'. A drop of 40 entries in the next year or two did not deter local farmers like G.E. Robinson of Moss End whose bull 'Wilbeth Futurist', originally from West Hall, Whittington, and cow 'Rex Dazzle' came out on top. By 1964 the Friesian class had grown to a new record of 108 entries which included newer winners such as F. Barnes of Ackenthwaite, and J.G. Charnley of Glasson Dock. In the non-pedigree class the main winner belonged to Miss Moyra Parsons of Overthwaite but as she was on holiday in Italy her champion beast had to be paraded by her mother. Next year when the same cow won again Moyra was present to lead it in the ring alongside cows from the herds of J.W. Melling, E. Ellis, F. Barnes and J. and J. Wightman. In 1967, Brucellosis reduced entries to 60 but by 1969 with 200 herds having 'passed the test' there was a good show when the top prize winners included the Society's Chairman H.H. Bell and the Vice Chairman Brian Ellis both of whom won in succeeding years when, among others, R. Willison and J. Leeming also had highlighted wins.

Gradually winning stock came from a wider area. In 1973 G.E. Robinson's and H.H. Bell's 'Farleton Polly 14th' and 'Holmeland Envy' though winners in their class had to yield supreme honours to 'Ullswater Beateux 4th' belonging to Ton Carrick of Eden Bank. In 1975 the male winner belonged to Maurice Wulfa of Great Salkeld. Over the years other farmers from the edge of the district who continued to do well included W.W. Jackson of Penrith, who also won the Webster cup for champion crossbreed, W.S. and P. Towers of Aldingham, John Moffat of Penrith, and J.H. Wilson of Thursby, Carlisle. By and large, however, the show's main Friesian awards went to local farmers such as the Robinsons, Bells, Ducketts and Willisons together with J.R. Leeming of Dalton, Maurice Wilson of Far Audlands and Roger Mason of Greenlands Farm, Tewitfield. In 1986 George Robinson of Moss End had a headlined win with 'Farleton Ideal Pandora' a five year old whose mother won the dry class. Three years later the press singled out another Farleton winner which had also won the Preston Farmers Dairy Stakes and the Milk Marketing Board awards. She was called

Early horned Friesian 'Holmland Ruby' and was a Friesian Holstein.

The rise of Holsteins in the 1980's threatened that the reign of the Friesians would be much shorter than that of their predecessors the Shorthorns. Already in 1982 and 1983 a new Holstein class was won by J.W. Melling and Son with 'Whipton Unique Tammy', a senior cow in milk which had calved five times but which also got the best udder award. So precious were the apparently large and robust Holsteins that Anthony Batty of Selside provided coats for his winning beasts 'Laithwaite Graceful' and 'Laithwaite Softly'. That those who had successfully reared other breeds were more than capable of moving with the times was soon demonstrated when Tommy Carrick won with 4 year old 'Ullswater Fanny' just before he retired while Bernard Parsons won his father's memorial trophy with 'Fairly Wychelm'. The early 1990's were dominated by the successes of Wilson, Joan and John Garnett of Ackenthwaite Farm whose 'Milnthorpe Athabaska Arnside' beat Richard Lawson's 'Deerslet Baron Lucky' in 1991 and then went on to win with others of the Ackenthwaite herd so that in 1992 the Garnets had had a champion cow on the field on eight occasions in the show season. By 1993 they had won the supreme dairy championships three years out of four. In 1995, however, much attention was paid to 'Supreme Twizzelfoot Conquest Val' belonging to John Battersby of Scales when it beat for first place Roy Batty's 'Light Water Topper Lily' by just one point. In 1997 the Ellis Perpetual Cup went to a four year old Holstein owned by Hubert Tinkler and his

George Robinson's Friesian champion 'Farleton Pansy' 1971
Photo: Westmorland Gazette

160

Holsteins supreme at the first 1992 Crooklands show. Dairy champion Arnside Athabaska with reserve Milnthorpe Rambo Clover 60th from W. Garnett's Ackenthwaite Farm Photo: Farmers Guardian

daughter Sheila of Lower Dean Farm, Ilkley and in 1998 the supreme champion 'Starcross Clara 15' came from John Sanderson's home bred herd from Kirkham, Lancashire.

By 1997 there were 1,672 animals 'on show at The Show' comprising 670 sheep, 335 horses, 202 goats and 345 cattle. The cattle classes represented a selection of breeds which had risen and declined in popularity over the last half century along with newcomers whose long term success was not as yet established. In the early post-war years it was Ayrshires which leavened the

show's display of Shorthorns and Friesians when winning entries came from W. Brooks-bank of The High Dairy Farm, Crosthwaite, C.A. Park of Broadgate farm, Windermere, J.T. Rawlinson of Lindale, G.M.

A fine Ayrshire at the 1997 show signified a revival of interest in the breed
Photo: Westmorland Gazette

Beck of Brougham, R. Armistead of Lambrigg with a rare aristocratic incursion, compared to earlier decades, from the Earl of Sefton's herd at Abbeystead. In 1951 S.K. Beck of Flodder hall, Lyth, who had only arrived from Wellington three months previously won with three year old 'Ellerton Eileen' which had never won before, and Mr Beck also won with his 10 month old bull 'Fairbank'. Other winning Ayrshire breeders were W.S. Watson of Carlisle, J. Knape of Crook and J.B. Cross of Meathop who among other successes had a top beast in 'Crown Bright Eyes' in 1961. But throughout their fifteen year pre-eminence the main honours for Ayrshires were divided between Mr Barnes and Mr Beck whose champions included, respectively, 'Barrower Spirit Level', 'Flodder Hall Rustic Gem' and 'Flodder Hall Faith 6th'. The last good year for Ayrshires was 1964 and in 1967 there were no entries at all. Thereafter their appearance was occasional and sporadic.

With a winning entry from A. Duckett in 1995 Jerseys were longer lasting but like the Ayrshires their heyday was in the 1950's and 1960's. In their first year at the show in 1954 the first prize went to J. Pattinson of Penrith and the only immediately local winner was E. Brook of Heversham. In 1955 Mrs I. Newall won with Mrs T.H. Telford, of Grasmere, the only Westmorland winner, taking second place. Another lady Mrs O.M. Cooper of Kirkby in Furness won in 1957. Then in 1958 father and daughter Mr D. and Miss Rose Kay entered their Jersey which they had reared, on a tiny small holding at Tewitfield, in their spare time from their everyday work, respectively, as a railwayman and telephonist. For them 1958 was not just a case of first time lucky as many prizes came their way over the next five or six years. Later Jersey winners included W.I. Raw of Galloway, B. Dickinson of Troutbeck, K.H. Paley of Brookhouse, Miss J.E. Pattinson of Windermere and J. and M. Exton of Goosnargh until in 1968 no Jerseys were entered at all.

It was also in the 1950's that Galloways (which had been present in the 1800's) reappeared at the show with winning entries from B. Dickinson of Kentmere, C.W. Garnett of Hawes, H. Gibson of High Helsfell and, in 1960, from the Earl of Lonsdale. In 1964 the championship was won by 17 year old Richard Allison of Hilton, Appleby whose father was the tenant of Midtown Farm 'but young Richard has his own stock'. Other regular winners at this time included W.N. Heaton of Hawkshead and W. Richardson of Laverock Bridge but there was a drop in entries in 1970 and none were reported after 1975.

First highlighted in 1965, when there were 17 entries, Herefords came relatively late on to the scene. At first the Richardsons of Laverock Bridge, R. Allonby of Windermere, Bryan Walling of Westview, Crosthwaite and E. Forshaw of Barbon were the more successful breeders. In 1973 G.W. and A.H. Dobson of Watermillock had a notable win with their 21 month old bull 'Paddock Gaylad' which they followed up with other successes over the next years with another bull 'Heather Hill Headlong'. A happy victory was achieved by F. Clayton of Chatburn who won the reserve championship in 1973 a week after he had missed his entry to Burton Show when his Range Rover broke down on the M6. In 1976 John Proctor's Canadian bull won first prize on its third birthday while in 1981 Bryan Walling had an important win with his heifer 'Many Springs Victor' which had been imported from Canada.

In the beef section Charolais bull (and cow) dozed aside most other breeds from the 1970's onwards. The first reported winners included a two year old bull 'Mount Pleasant Granada' belonging to A.T. Goodland, Ambleside in 1973 and other top bulls belonging respectively to G.W. and H. Dobson, Miss A. Harrison and Mr H.E. Barton of Meathop - who won on his first showing of Charolais in 1975. G. Ashburner and Sons of Millom, Bernard Parsons, Tucker Mason of Helsington, A. Stapleton of Penrith, and W.D. Tyson of Keswick, Tom Cornthwaite of Low hall, Tarn Green and Tom Owen of Bold, Cheshire also had important wins. The Charolais' supreme quality was firmly attested when for the first time ever in 1981 a beef cow 'Kelton Celeste' belonging to David Grant of Gelston Castle Farms won the General Stock Championship.

The Charolais main rivals in beef were Limousins first shown in four classes in 1979 when the main winners were W.G. Case of Barrow, A.S. Fenton of Lancaster, and J.M. Thompson of Melmerby. In 1981 when Johnny Thompson won with 18 month old 'Radar' he explained that the Limousins' lean meat was 'just what the housewife needed'. In later years he had repeated wins including a double win in 1991 and a champion beast with 'Hartside Davina' in 1992. 1993 saw the Kendal Business Park Trophy go to 'Oakleigh Asterix' belonging to Graham Simms of Northwich. That the Westmorland Show was the nation wide shop window for Limousin was, however, more firmly established when in 1996 the show hosted the first Limousin Derby in the country.

It was, however, in the names of the latest breeds that many international notes were struck at the show. Newer breeds introduced included Blonde Aquitaine in 1982. A notable example of the breed was 'Blonde D'Aquitaine Alpath Vera' shown by Tucker Mason in 1988 though the supreme Championship went to G.W. Dale & C. Dale of Sandbach, Cheshire. In 1989 Billy Swainson 'who had never won a sash before' had a prize bull 'Greenoak Dynamic' and in 1991 a widely praised beast was 'Bromfield Diamond' belonging to Mr J. Taylor and Mrs Leeming of Ulverston.

To all the Friesians, Charolais, Limousins and Aquitaines were added in the show's twentieth decade Piedmontese Blue, Belgium Blue, Salers and Simmentals. The latter class was won in 1998 by a simmental bull 'Rosten Ginger' valued at £5,000 which belonged to Bill Heaps, a scrap dealer from Chorley. Truly in every respect the cattle classes were changing.

As in cattle the show's sheep classes both expanded and diversified. A broad difference, however, was that there was much less change in the popularity of the breeds comparable to the switches from Shorthorns to Friesians and thence on to Holsteins. Moreover, the old Westmorland Rough Fell breeds retained their popularity as did, despite one lull, the Dales breed. Indeed there was very much a pre-war savour about the 1940's Sheep classes with the bulk of the attention being given to the winners of the Sir Samuel Scott trophy for Rough Fells and the Rough Fell Sheep Breeders Association bowl, both of which were taken by old sheep breeding families like the Dargues of Forest Hall and the Grisedales of Selside. On the other hand there was praise for Wensleydales bred by B. Farrer of Grange in 1946 and to J. Dargue of Burneside 'who always never fails to produce magnificent Wensleydales' in 1947. W.A. Parkinson of Quernmore also showed a Champion Wensleydale tup in 1948 while in the same year popular wins were reported for a Half Bred ram belonging to Mark Fawcett and Sons of Burton in Lonsdale, fine Swaledales from W.N. Dargue's Forest Hall flock and Rough Fells belonging to Mr J. Capstick of Brownber, Ravenstonedale.

'There was the best ever show of roughs' in 1950 but, the reporter added 'the Teeswaters are the up and coming breed which is an improvement on the Wensleydale'. Teeswaters were also 'becomingly increasingly popular for breeding half bred lambs by using a Teeswater ram on horned ewes'. From the start such Teesdale breeders as F. Tarn of Winston, J.R. Addison of Mickleton, Barnard Castle and especially the Bainbridge family of near Richmond virtually made the class their own and they or their descendants were still winning 40 years later. Sometimes the success was achieved against the odds as when J.R. Addison won with a champion ewe which had nearly died of pneumonia in the savage winter of 1963. Later on the Teesdale victors were occasionally beaten by competitors from elsewhere like H. Hinde of Harrogate, J.R. Meelin of Helifield, and from the show district, A.W. Benson of Barbon, M. Brownrigg of

Teeswaters

Kirkby Stephen and R.T. Gibson and Son of Low Audlands, Endmoor.

Although 'all sections were in full bloom' at the 1950 show the Wensleydales were well down and by 1953 their entry had been over taken by 50 Teeswaters. A few local breeders like M. Airey of Lancaster and T. Burton of Arrad Foot persisted with the breed until 1959 when no championships were awarded though 'an odd one or two appeared every now and again' in later years.

Swaledales were more enduring and there were generally about 70 entries at the shows in the 1950's when the main winners were A. Harker and Son of Leyburn, Messrs Dargue of Selside and the Dixons of Hawes. Numbers dropped to a handful in 1969 and the class was more or less dormant in the1970's and then in 1980 it was announced that the 'Swaledale Championship has been won by a farmer who also owns a transport café'. He was Mr Laurie Raine of the Coach and Horses farm, Spital. Despite the implied sneer the Raines went on to produce scores of other champions and in 1988 Neville Raine paid £10,000 for a ram. Possessing a 'very good colour, good head, good looking horns, good coloured coat and good legs' it could fairly be described as being - 'good' - especially as it 'had won back its price tag in its first season'. The Raines' supremacy was occasionally dented as when Alan M. Wilson of Middleton in Teesdale (but formerly of Selside) and Derek Sowerby of Hilton, Appleby, won the Swaledale championships in 1987. Even so the shepherds 'from the transport café' went on winning well into the 1990's.

To most folk the sheep sections at the show meant Roughs and the ever

G. M. Sedgwick of Sedbergh with champion Rough Fell ram 1970

popular Herdwicks. Moreover the names of the winning owners indicate that fell folk are every bit as tenacious in holding on to their heritage as are the sheep on their native heath. Throughout the 1950's a regular champion was Mr J. Hudson from Black Moss, Windermere but other successful breeders included R. Nicholson of Cookson's Tenement Howgill, R. Batty of Selside Hall, A. Dixon, Kit Cragg, Selside, C. Gibson of Burneside Hall, J.T. Postlethwaite of Ridings, Howgill, T. Harper and Sons of Ghyll Farm, Sedbergh, R. Armistead of Lambrigg, M. Bateman of Beckfoot and from over to the west T. Wilson of Tarn Green, Cartmel Fell. Accidents could happen and in 1955 'a curious happening' was reported. 'Mr J.T. Postlethwaite completely overlooked the fact that his gimmer lambs could be entered for the best Fell Sheep irrespective of sex with the result that another female sheep belonging to Mr T. Wilson won'. Undaunted Mr Postlethwaite went on to win again along with other eastern fells farmers who from the late fifties were being challenged for first place by the Capstick family. In 1964 when there were 300 entries for Roughs G.H. Capstick of Birkshaw, Howgill won seven championships with one ram notching up its 17th title while in 1964 A. and D.B. Capstick of Newbiggin on Lune won with an aged ram and, incidentally, also took a first for his shearling Blue Faced Leicester ram. A similar champion was W.D. Tyson whose 'Blencathra Fenwick' took its 100th first for Herdwicks in 1967. Around the mid 1970's K. and G. Allison of Park House, Ravenstonedale and E. Dargue of Dufton, Appleby (who paid £2,000 for one Rough ram) took back to Eden District the Rough Fell breeders cup, the Sir Samuel Scott, the Tebay Farmers bowl, and several other trophies. Also from the eastern side of the area J.A. Alderson of Stainmore and Ian Mallinson of Winton also did well while from the west Tyson Hartley of Broughton in Furness also put up an effective attempt to stop Lakeland shepherds from monopolising the Rough championships. As proof that the Rough tradition was being passed on twenty year old Anthony Hartley who farmed with his father Tyson at Turner Hall, Seathwaite won with three shear home bred Herdwicks in 1982. Ten years later, no longer quite so young, Anthony was still scooping the prizes when he beat Gowain Grave (who despite many successes as a farmer the *Gazette* called a 'haulage driver'!) for the Herdwick Championship. Moving the show down to Crooklands had no effect on the popularity of the Roughs and in 1997, for instance, excellent winning sheep were on show from the flocks of the Hartleys, Norman Dodd of Flakebridge, Tebay and Geoff and Roger Sedgwick who, in 1998 bought the Rough champion for only 50 guineas. It was a mark both of inflation and of the continuing importance of the Roughs that this was considered to be a 'reasonable price'.

The Dales sheep class is easy to summarise. Whereas in most other breeds it is almost impossible to give even a broad selection of leading exhibitors at the show, in Dales the leading champion breeder from the 1960's to the 1990's was

Bob Bindloss of Grayrigg Hall

Bob Bindloss' champion Dalesbred tup
Ian Johnson Photography

Robert Bindloss of Grayrigg Hall who after more than a generation of success had lost count of the number of prizes he had won. Not that 't'owd Bob allus hed et his own way' for his successful competitors included the Dixons of Kit Cragg, and the Smith Brothers of Clapham who pipped Mr Bindloss to the post in the 1990 championship.

Half Bred Sheep continued to be shown throughout most of the period though never in great numbers. In the 1950's their classes attracted winners from quite far away like P. Sherwin of Bedale. Local winners included H. Cottam of New Hutton who won with a 'cross from a black faced Mountain or Herdwick ewe' in 1958, Mrs Gladys Dean of Town End, Crosthwaite who won in 1963 and, another lady, Mrs Coulthurst of Gargrave who won in 1968.

Lowland breeds were present at the shows in the 1940's and 1950's but it was not until the 1960's that they seemed to have become prominent. In 1970 some attention was paid to R. Stirzaker of Milnthorpe winning with his Suffolks which he repeated several times in the next ten years. In 1974 the Blue Faced Leicester champion belonged to Mr M. Harvey of Low House, Claughton, Lancashire but the reserve came from the flock of Sidney Watson of Farleton who subsequently presented a cup for the breed. In 1978 Ian Little, of Helm Croft, Barrows Green, won both with his Mules and his Leicesters while in 1982 John Harrison of Wickerfield, Kings Meaburn was featured with his Suffolk gimmer lambs and Leicesters. From the north three different members of the Harrison family from around Penrith scooped prizes for Blue Faced Leicesters, Suffolks and Rouge de L'Ouest. The latter were just one of several rarer or rarefied breeds that came

Sid Watson with champion Leicester 1977

*Mrs Margaret Capstick with
'Musgrove Rosalind' c.1955*

in at the end of the period which included Texels introduced in 1982. Of the 'rarefieds' by far the most attractive to the general public have been the curly horned Jacob Sheep introduced in 1980 when Mrs MacCartney of Capernwray won the first of many firsts for the breed.

Happily at the 1998 show there was ample evidence that while not all the old 'fell' breeds were holding their own the fell shepherds had not lost their taste for experimentation. It was perhaps significant that the lowland champion Suffolk (which had cost 750 guineas) had been bred not by a shepherd but by a shepherdess Sandra Ireton of Chapel-Le-Dale and that the sheep now belonged to G.M. Sedgwick and Sons who had formerly been renowned mainly for their Rough Fells.

Sheep and goats may go together in popular parlance but it was only in 1955 that both species were exhibited at the show when largely at the instigation of Mrs Margaret Capstick of Old Hutton a goat class was started. In that year apart from Mrs Capstick the main winners, setting a trend for the future, were also ladies and included Miss Jane Ramsbottom of Caton and Miss P. Thornton of Dalston.

'Show kids'
Westmorland Gazette

Soon show goers were to get used to such bizarre terms as Female Toggenburg, British Saanen and British Alpine but for the next decade or so entries were only around 40 and dropped to 29 in 1960. The class attracted many 'offcomers' and Miss J. Mostyn Owen from Borough Bridge, Mrs Harben from Gomersall and A.E. Stottard of Harrogate showed regularly alongside a handful of local exhibitors. Then in 1975 there was a 50% increase to 90 and four years later there were 124 separate exhibitors some of whom had travelled from Newcastle, Southern Scotland and Humberside. Eastern county exhibitors did particularly well with, for instance, a champion British Alpine female 'Silverline Francesca' winning for Mr Richard Wood of Newcastle in 1981; 'Tea Time Polly' who won in 1988 belonged to Mr Peter Copeland of Bishop Auckland while the British goat champion 'Aphrodite Annacicone' belonged to Elaine Woodmass also from Bishop Auckland in 1992. Despite occasional ups and downs - a drop in entries was attributed to a rise in petrol prices in 1982 - the section became highly regarded as well as very popular with the general public. 'You can't really

Judging ponies 1977

get much better' was the opinion of the chief steward Mrs Marina Chapman in 1986, 'we have the best goats in the north of England'. She wasn't kidding and by 1998 with quality and numbers growing this opinion would have had to be amended to the 'best in the country'.

Popular as were goats with the public their attraction was always less than that for horses which rose in popularity as their use for serious agricultural purposes disappeared. In 1946 the *Gazette* report still contained a semblance of former times: 'there was one of the best collections of Shires and Clydesdales

Miniature ponies for the very young. Eileen Ellis at the 1997 show

seen in the northern ring showing that the Westmorland farmer still prides himself on his horses in spite of the increasing popularity of tractors'. Following their success with Shorthorns the Clydesdales winners were Messrs Harrison of Cliburn with W. Garnett of Ackenthwaite in reserve. There were also firsts for the pre-war winners the Newhouses of Slyne. By 1948 there were only 18 entries in eight classes and no entries in two classes. No one, however, doubted the quality of the winners, notably a gelding belonging to Irving Holiday of Clifton Hall and a brood mare shown by J. Parsons of Ambleside and fine hunters brought to the ring by Miss J. Temple of Kendal and W. McLung of Lockerbie. The next four or five years saw wins by good horses for the Newhouses and Parsons but always they were shown in an ever more depleted field. In 1951 there were only 27 horses both agricultural and recreational on the field 'reflecting the steady march of mechanisation' and incidentally explaining why many people (like the present author) brought up in the South Westmorland of the early 1950's have never even sat on a horse. Except at the seaside there were not even donkeys in the area although in 1968 when 'Lucy', 'Tich' and 'Michael' from Bardsea appeared at the show there have been Donkey classes on the schedule.

For a few more years breeders of 'heavies' like the Newhouses and Parsons were joined by other exhibitors such as J. Cottam of Milnthorpe and H. Hallhead of Nether Kellett who won four classes in 1955 but when there were 17 entries in 1956 it was hailed as a rebirth for the breed. This renaissance did not last and numbers went down to nothing ten years later. Then in 1973 having been dropped altogether for five years the agricultural class was revived and by 1975 it was reported that there were '31 heavy horses which is remarkable in an age of mechanisation where such animals are kept in the main for nostalgic and breeding purposes'. Moreover with 400 horses altogether at the Show it was claimed that 'there are now more horses in England than ever before'. In the 'heavy' classes the main awards went to R. Livesey and Sons, A. Wilkinson and to Thwaites Brewery of Blackburn whose parading drays were probably better value as regards the rural beer market than a television commercial. In 1977 there were a 'staggering' 69 heavies on show but the numbers dropped the next year to only 34 following the death of the previous principal organiser Mr J.R. Ward of Weeton. At the 1981 show horses, at 378, out numbered sheep at 366 and cattle at 321 and in 1983 there were six well filled classes setting a burgeoning trend which attracted all comers in the 1990's when for instance a popular winner for a heavy Shire mare was 'Trofarth Wendy' belonging to Ann Scott of Akhead caravan site in 1994.

'Light' horses, hunters and ponies especially Fell Ponies competing for the Mrs Somervell cup quickly had full classes. Representative winners included Colonel Houldsworth - hunters 1947-53, Mrs Sanderson - part Arab bred 1947,

Mrs B. Stothert (formerly Miss Barbara Temple) in the Private Driving class driving a curved panel Phaeton, made in 1907 by Kelly of Bowness and the mare 'Mayfly' bred by the owner c.1947

British Palomino Rosette, Mrs Clark 1959, Briary Close part Arab bred Trophy, Miss Alexander 1959, Mr J. Bell, Wigton, Native Bred 1964, G. Williamson of Broughton Fell, and Mr and Mrs E.S. Cumber of Middlesbrough, light horses in 1989. Thanks to many enthusiasts like Richard Dobson a long time organiser and life member of the Show Jumping Association by the late eighties hardly a report appeared that did not mention the names of riders, whose prowess had been demonstrated at the show and who were currently taking part in national and international events. Leading 'eventers' who did well at the show in more recent times included Rebecca Knipe described as being from 'Elsington', Francis Haysmith, Stephen Garrod and Anne McCutcheon who all won prizes in 1993. In 1995 Janet Wilson from Staveley won the open riding on her hunter 'Flo Jo', the intermediate prize went to Emma Boardman of Yealand on 'Valentina' and the junior to Hannah Quatermain on 'Causeway Minuet'. Always the junior events have been a good way of introducing younger people to wider responsibilities at the show and in 1996, for instance, Judith Buckley nee Edmonson, after 25 years of competing, became the Horse Steward for the show. Sometimes the riders' enthusiasm for the show might have gone a little too far as regards their other commitments as when Jayne Gill of Beast Banks reportedly returned home from honeymoon, so that she could enter her horse 'Birkby Marksman' in the open hunter class. Fortunately she and he won so hopefully her husband (the other 'he') Graham would be pleased as well.

Strangely it was motoring that led to the expansion of recreational riding as it enabled townsfolk to drive out to riding schools or, as they became known, 'equitation centres' and also to much sought after paddocks in the countryside while the light horse box pulled behind the family car enabled Mum and Dad (but mainly Mum) to convey their offspring to gymkhanas and riding events. Amongst local equestrians hunting continued to mean very little though local 'hunters' figured prominently at the County Show.

Young riders 1959,
Sarah Temple, Cecilia Temple and Giles Stothert

In the immediate post-war years the light horse and riding events were for an exclusive minority. At the 1946 Show Gymkhana, which was reported almost as a novelty event, most attention was paid to a human as 'in the only (*sic*) accident Master Hugo Wakefield, younger son of Mr and Mrs E.B. Wakefield of the Old House, Stricklandgate was thrown from his pony when he reared.' No doubt without his parents' permission he was then 'helped back to the saddle and pluckily completed his class after which he was examined by a doctor and found to have cracked a collar bone'. Fortunately such character building 'pluck' soon, however, went out of fashion when the riding classes, in every sense, expanded so that no show was complete without a whole bevy of juvenile riders careering in only simulated danger round the ring in the musical chairs, tyre, potato and apple races. In the immediate post-war years many of the leading riders came from outside the county. Leading juveniles included Teddy Clark of Penrith, J.R.W. Calvert of Richmond, Miss E. Nuttall of Withnell and Miss E. Ellis of Bingley but by the sixties local riders outnumbered and often outranked those from away and included J.E. Fell of Troutbeck, in 1968, and Caroline Swift of Brookhouse in 1971. Even so in the bumper year 1986 when the leading child rider Jayne Wilson of Crook won on 'Keston Poldark' she was reported as doing so 'for Mr and Mrs Flannagan of Moberley, Cheshire.' In the local pony event 'for riders living within 15 miles of Kendal' the winner was Karen Allonby of Grayrigg on 'Hot Gossip'.

Adult leaping events continued to provide thrills and spills but throughout the period riders from all over the country outnumbered local participants. In the early fifties, however, G. Dickinson from Haverthwaite, E. Beck of Hornby and G.A. Beck of Stainton, Penrith won regularly but the main champions nevertheless included W. McLung of Lockerbie and Col R.D. Houldsworth of Firth, Roxburgh.

Balancing horse classes which provided most of the 'entertainment' at the show two sections which expanded at the post-war shows firmly emphasised that the 'Westmorland County' was still rooted firmly on the farm - or at least in the farm yard. Poultry had been taken into account in the general Farm Stock classes as early as the 1800's and separate shows took place for many years on the same day as the main show but it was not until the 1960's that poultry became important classes in their own right. Moreover they attracted some of the show's youngest competitors and in 1983 14 year old Stephen Horn of Natland was reported as having won a 'feather for his cap' when he took half a dozen firsts for his fowls. Another younger winner was 22 year old Richard Rawell of Westhouse with a barred hen. By 1986 with 240 entries the poultry section was 'the best anybody could remember' with 'animals' (this really was the term used!) coming from all over the country. In that year the overall winner was Mr E. Kirkbride of Northumberland but local champions soon came forward of whom the most successful were Messrs Bennett and Bainbridge of Burton and J.T. Metcalf of Gatebeck. Invariably the quality of the birds was high although, as the poultry secretary Ken Simpson explained in the 1980's 'it was not a good time of year as most of the birds are in moult and are a long way off getting their winter coats'. In 1991 for instance most of the birds belonging to Alex Cuthbertson (who had been called 'King of Kendal' by a poultry magazine) were moulting but he still managed to win with a four month old Leghorn. Another successful bird man was Crook farmer George Taylor who was presented with the Poultry Society's highest award as he had won more than 30 gold cards. Even more noteworthy was the report that 'the eggs he shows are not just the usual white and brown eggs but include some green eggs from the more exotic species!'

To a timorous stranger the farmyard cur is the least exotic of local species but when carefully bred and trained no canine can outshine the intelligence or beauty of the Lakeland or Border Collie which perhaps as much as the Herdwicks and the Shorthorns deserves to be ranked as Westmorland's most historically important animal. In the early post-war shows the dogs section had all manner of breeds of which various types of spaniel and terrier were the most popular though in 1949 the *Gazette* reported almost in a surprised note 'there were many sheep dogs competing'. Later terriers dominated the Kennel Club sections and a quarter of an hour was even allocated on the main Show Day programme to 'terrier racing'.

In the immediate post-war years the main canine element was provided by the Hound Trails which closed Show Day on an exciting note with a final chase down Benson Knott. There were trails for juniors and seniors. In 1950 the senior trail attracted 122 and the junior 22 which were won respectively in 33 minutes, 22 seconds and 17 minutes 59 seconds. By 1956 the Senior times had been shaved to 30 minutes 47 seconds but the Junior never bettered the 17 minute mark. After a lull in entrants the trail was revived when Vaux Brewery offered a £100 prize in 1962 which was increased to £150 in the next year when 46 hounds took place in a trail ranging through Skelsmergh, Patton, Docker, Benson Knott and Jenkin Cragg. During the later 1960's hound trailing declined in popularity and the traffic hazard caused when scores of hounds were crossing the main roads around Kendal during the tea time rush hour created growing problems for the organisers so the event became less prominent and it was not revived when the show moved out to Crooklands.

There were also occasional lulls and problems with the dog championship classes. Even so when in 1975, because of difficulties on the field, the section had to be shown at Longlands School 230 dogs were entered in 64 classes to which in 1979, according to the long serving secretary, Mrs E. Farrer a new class for Schipperkes (which attracted 14 entries) was added. There was a slight drop in entries in subsequent years but in 1984 '150 dogs braved the rain' when the 'top dog' was a whippet belonging to Mrs M. Stanley of Witherslack and the best puppy 'Moon beam of Byrock' was shown by Mrs E. Wright of Westgate. Most of the well filled classes had at least a nominal country connection and included those for German Shepherds, Bearded Collies, any variety of Collie, Corgies, Guide dogs group, Setters, Spaniels - Cocker, sporting and Springers, Retrievers, Dachshunds, any variety of hounds, pointers, Bull breeds and Tibetans. Lakeland and Westmorland breeds happily were still doing well in the most recent shows with 'Pickle' who 'hunts with the Coniston pack' being the champion Fox Hound in 1992. In subsequent years local terriers such as 'Bonnie' belonging to Jack and Silvia Dewhurst beat all comers who had been drawn from as far away as Scotland, Newcastle and the Midlands.

Thus for dogs, as for every other class, the Westmorland County Show had won nation wide renown by serving more than just the old County whose ever honoured name it perpetuates.

And finally a reminder -
Any account of any aspect of agriculture is primarily a human story.
'Not so rough' - a good show for the Capsticks of Birkshaw and their
Rough Fell sheep 1981

✳   ✳   ✳

INDEX

177

FROM FELL AND FIELD

Wellheads/Well Heads 76
Wensleydale Sheep 82,
111, 112, 114, 164 et seq.
West Hall 159
West William 11
Westgate 175
Westhouse 82
Westmeringas 7
Westmorland 7 et seq.
Westmorland Agricultural
School (Newton Rigg) 73
Westmorland Centre 9
Westmorland Confederation
of Womens Institutes 118
Westmorland County Agri-
cultural Society Ltd., 131
Westmorland Gazette 9, 80,
90, 98, 122, 135
Westmorland Gazette
Shield 99, 148, 149, 150
Westmorland General
hospital 9
Westmorland Show 9 et seq.
Westmorland Volunteers
66
Westmorland Woollen
Company 101
Westmorland Wills 15 et seq.
Weston Freda 99
Weston Col./Sir John MP 91,120
Westview (Crosthwaite)
162
Wharton H 111
Wharton J D C 114
Wharton Lord 17
Wheat 27
Whitehall 86
'Whitehall' (potato) 103
Whiteside Messrs 69
'Whipton Unique Tammy'
(cow) 160
Whittington 41, 159
Whittle Misses 150
Whitwell Alderman 56
Whitwell Mr & Mrs Arthur
130
Whitwell Captain 86
Whitwell E 115
Whittaker family 68

Whittaker Mr 114
Whittaker Mr C 132
Wickerfield 167
Wightman J and J 159
Wightman R 143
Wigton 56, 109, 171
'Wilbeth' (cow) 159
Wildman Mr C 132
Wilkinson A 171
Wilkinson Muriel 153
Wills 15, 24, 26
Wills John 45
Williams John 131, 135
Williamson G 172
Williamson George 25, 32
Williamson J S 143
Williamson Messrs 69, 70
Willink A H 90
Willison family 20, 34, 159
Willison Mr B 132
Willison Mr J M 132
Willison Henry & Nora
147, 148, 149
Willison Mr. 41
Willison Richard 44, 47, 49,
50, 53, 63
Willison Robert 68, 153,
156, 159
Wilson family 34
Wilson C 72
Wilson C H 84
Wilson C W 73
Wilson Christopher 37
Wilson Daniel 34, 37, 42,
48, 53
Wilson George 41, 42, 63,
67
Wilson James 24, 86
Wilson Jayne 173
Wilson John/'Johnny' 106,
107, 115
Wilson J H 159
Wilson T 47, 166
Wilson W 82
Winsford 158
Winton 166
Winston 164
Witherslack 15, 18, 127, 175
Witherslack Court Roles 34

Witherslack Hall 49
Witton family 3
'Wild Rosebud 8th' (cow) 108
Windermere 15, 34, 92, 99,
127, 142, 145, 161, 162,
166
Windermere Railway 64
Windermere Show 63
Windsor Royal Show 106
Winster 15, 34, 115
Withnell 173
Wordsworth William 17, 20,
21
Wood family 123
Wood J A 127
Wood Joseph 111, 112, 113
Wood Mrs M F 132
Wood Richard 168
Woodmass Elaine 168
Woods Mrs 147
Woof James 84, 106, 109
Woof W 89, 92
Wool 80
Women's Institutes 98, 121,
129, 140, 144, 145 et seq.
Women's Land Army (see
also Land Girls) 123, 124
Workhouse Drum and Fife
Band 66
Workington Show 39
Wrestling Cumberland &
Westmorland 135, 136
Wright Elizabeth 25
Wright John 77
Wright Miss E 175
Wulfa Maurice 159
Wyndsoeur William de 31
Wyresdale 68

Young Farmers' Clubs
(YFC's) 99, 143, 148 et seq.
Y.W.C.A. 98
Yealand 81, 172
Yeates H 47, 47
Yorkshire 9, 114
Yorkshire Show The Great
64, 94, 158
Young Arthur 47
Young Mr 86

PRINT PREPARATION BY CARNMOR PRINT & DESIGN, PRESTON, UK
PRINTED BY ST. EDMUNDSBURY PRESS, BURY ST. EDMUNDS